Mixing oil and water

MEDICAL LIBRARY
HEMEL HEMPSTEAD HOSPITAL
HILLFIELD ROAD
HEMEL HEMPSTEAD
HERTS HP2 4AD

Mixing oil and water

How can primary care organisations improve health as well as deliver effective health care?

Geoffrey Meads, Professor of Health Services Development, Health Management Group, City University, London (Project Leader)

Amanda Killoran, Head of Development, Health Education Authority, London

John Ashcroft, Research Director, Relationships Foundation, Cambridge

Yvonne Cornish, Senior Lecturer, South East Institute for Public Health, Kent

ISBN 0 7521 1655 X

Trevelyan House
30 Great Peter Street
London SW1P 2HW
www.hea.org.uk
Designed by Edwin Belchamber
Printed in Great Britain

Contents

Appendices

Foreword

Perspectives from project participants

Primary care has been subjected to a number of reforms in the past. These reforms have generally resulted in different ways of doing things. They have largely influenced how we work at an operational level. The reforms creating primary care groups (PCGs) will influence primary care in a much more fundamental way. It will change *why* we do things. Primary care has no option now but to involve itself at a strategic level. General practice has been an autonomous profession, responding to demand, priding itself that by using personal clinical judgement it promises the best care to each patient it faces. Primary care groups challenge every part of this notion. General practice must now be part of a wider democracy, looking for need, performing evidence-based medicine. Most importantly, it must work towards creating a service that offers the most benefits to the most people. This potentially compromises the care to an individual.

The PCG responsibility for improving the health of populations as well as caring for individuals leaves no option but to adopt a public health role. If we are to succeed in integrating our local clinical experience with public health expertise and existing knowledge of commissioning services, and draw all these together to create a Health Improvement Programme that will deliver the objectives of The new NHS, we must have a robust relationship with our health authority.

Good or bad, we often take our relationship with the health authority for granted. Taking part in the project described in this report, I have used the tools that explore that relationship objectively. Once the weaknesses in the relationship can be shown in a rational way, you can then plan (hopefully together) to improve that relationship.

Within the project I have also had the privilege of glimpsing the future. Theoretical models of primary care organisations were played through with interesting results. Not all of what was seen was pleasant, but if these models help us realise our potential whilst showing which pitfalls to predict and avoid, we will be better prepared for the future.

I believe in primary care, and I believe that if we get our relationships right, our organisations healthy and our public involved, primary care groups will make a significant impact on reducing the many inequalities we experience and improve the health of our population. This report can help us on our way.

Chris James, GP and Chairman,
Southampton City Primary Care Group

'Promoting and improving the health of the population.'

Many individuals and many organisations feel they have a role, even a leading role, in this. However, it can be surprising how soon, and how much, there is divergence of opinion once one delves more deeply into what this might mean.

Over recent years in England increasing recognition has been given to the importance of primary care in ensuring the public health. Already, those terms 'primary care' and 'public health' are slippery with different meanings for different parties, as is made clear in this report. To what extent are 'primary care' and 'general practice' synonymous, or even related? Is 'public health' the domain of certain trained professionals, or is it everybody's business?

This report describes, from many points of view, the anxieties, challenges and opportunities in current attempts to ensure that developing primary care organisations do have an appropriate focus on the public health. It tells a story of mixed success; offers new ways of thinking about the tensions and the responses; and gives pointers to the future. It clarifies the potential and the risks.

The future may well be as turbulent as the present. Those who aim to shape it will need to keep a firm vision of their fundamental values, while being flexible enough to adapt and meld strategies and structures to the ever changing needs.

Barry Tennison
Director of Public Health, West Hertfordshire Health Authority,
(and former GP)

Preface

This is a report of an 18-month project that was designed to explore how primary care organisations can improve health as well as deliver effective health care. Overall it is an optimistic report, sometimes surprisingly so. We did not, for example, expect to meet general medical practitioners and others with such specific local visions for primary health care and tangible illustrations of its principles of inter-agency working and community involvement and its desire to address inequalities. Similarly there were some impressive examples of multidisciplinary, cross-directorate and inter-organisational commitments by some health authorities to public health. Clearly there is a great deal of unrecognised good practice in respect of primary health care in England simply waiting to be disclosed – and exploited.

This report is also, however, a cautionary tale. The story it tells shows how far there is still to travel on the road to synergy between primary care and public health. That health strategy and its effective implementation are a relational process is easy to write; much more difficult to understand and internalise; and even harder to reward in practice.

The working relationships required need substantial amounts of time, skills, education and, above all, perseverance; all of which are often in short supply in the contemporary National Health Service (NHS). The latter is, as the description of local breakdowns on all sides in the following narrative illustrates, often subsumed by short-term operational pressures and perspectives. 'Primary health care' is a definition of primary care that captures the potential of primary care's contribution to securing community health improvements. Primary health care, with its potential for promoting wider public health, is the long view. It requires those now working in primary care actually to become strategic. In some places this will be for the first time. The NHS faces a major challenge to its capacity for organisational development.

Part of this challenge is about adjusting mindsets. The basic principle of 'Equity for health' is the best example. For primary care professionals in the past equity has often been divisive. Its application has actually meant resource competitions between general practices for separate services on the grounds of achieving equitable access for individual patients. That equitable health status requires not simply co-operation between general practices but a whole host of other organisations as well, is a tough lesson to take on, particularly as many of these organisations fall well outside the conventional boundaries of the public service sector.

A readiness to try to learn such tough lessons has been a characteristic of many of the local participants in this project. Inevitably this has produced tensions. At times it was like mixing oil and water. Re-orienting towards local community health issues, so that the unit of primary care starts to see itself as a community organisation, was a shift in mindsets that challenged the research team as much as it did professional managers and practitioners. To both are due thanks for the learning generated. We hope the report does justice to their endeavours and qualifies as a genuine service of transferable learning to those now also engaged on the path to primary health care.

Geoff Meads
Professor of Health Services Development, City University, London

Acknowledgements

We are grateful to all project participants; the network of district teams that contributed their expertise, experience and time to addressing this difficult but rewarding question. We are also grateful for the advice from the NHS Executive. On a personal note special thanks are due to Susan Sweeney for her work on the manuscript.

Project participants

Contributions to the project were made by local primary care organisations and health authorities from the following districts:

- Barking and Havering
- Calderdale and Kirklees
- Dorset
- Leeds
- North and Mid-Hampshire
- North Cheshire
- North West Anglia
- Nottinghamshire
- Southampton and South West Hampshire
- Suffolk
- West Hertfordshire
- West Pennine.

Abbreviations

CHIMP	Commission for Health Improvement
CHS	Community health services
DPH	Director of public health
GMS	General medical services
GPC	General Practice Committee
GPCG	General practice commissioning group
GPFH	General practice fundholding
HA	Health authority
HAZ	Health Action Zone
HCHS	Hospital and community health services
HFA	Health For All
HLC	Healthy Living Centre
HImP	Health Improvement Programme
HoN	*The Health of the Nation* (1992 government White Paper)
HNA	Health needs assessment
HP	Health promotion
LA	Local authority
LMC	Local medical committee
MDS	Minimum datasets
NHS	National Health Service
NHSE	National Health Service Executive
NICE	National Institute for Clinical Excellence
NSF	National Service Framework
OHN	*Our healthier nation* (1998 government Green Paper)
ONS	Office of National Statistics
PAMS	Professions allied to medicine
PCAP	(1997) Primary Care Act Pilot
PCG	Primary care group
PCO	Primary care organisation
PCT	Primary Care Trust
PGE	Postgraduate Education
PHC	Primary health care
RCGP	Royal College of General Practitioners
SLA	Service Level Agreement
SSD	Social services department
SRB	Single Regeneration Budget
TPP	Total Purchasing Pilot
WHO	World Health Organization

1. The starting point: primary care and the public health agenda

Aim and objectives of the project

The overall aim of this developmental project was to draw lessons on how primary care groups (PCGs) can improve the wider public health as well as deliver effective health care, based on the experience of leading edge primary care organisations in transition to becoming PCGs.

The project was established in the autumn of 1997 in recognition of the trends in primary care-led commissioning which meant that GPs and others working in primary care had an increasingly important role to play in developing and implementing local health strategies. The new government's early expressed intentions to take forward a broad public health agenda, and to build on developments in primary care, highlighted the need to consider how primary care could be supported in developing its contribution to community health improvement and tackling inequalities.

The new public health strategy for England is expressed through a range of developments and initiatives including the creation of a Minister for Public Health, the Green Paper, *Our healthier nation* (Department of Health, 1998a), Health Action Zones (HAZs) and Healthy Living Centres. Public health goals are central to the reforms of *The new NHS* (Department of Health, 1998b) and *Modern local government* (Department of Environment, Transport and the Regions, 1998). The modernisation agenda sets the new framework for developing and implementing local Health Improvement Programmes (HImPs). New primary care groups have explicit responsibility for promoting the health of their local communities and tackling inequalities in health. This project was designed to explore the potential role of PCGs in bringing about community health improvement, through drawing on the experience of a range of primary care organisations (for example, Total Purchasing Pilots, Locality Commissioning Pilots).

The term primary care organisations (PCOs) was used as the project was undertaken in a period of transition during which the precise nature and configuration of PCGs locally was being discussed and planned.

The objectives were:

- To help health authorities and primary care organisations explore effective ways of working together to develop and implement Health Improvement Programmes and community health action programmes to make progress towards health improvement targets
- To define the potential role of primary care organisations in improving the health of their local communities, and the organisational competencies and support that are required to fulfil this role effectively
- To inform future policy development on the contribution PCGs could make to *Our healthier nation.*

As indicated above, the project was conceived before publication of the Green Paper, *Our healthier nation* and the White Paper, *The new NHS.* Its original emphasis was on whether or not primary care organisations *could* promote public health as well as deliver health care. However, the brief was subsequently amended to focus more on *how* this would be possible, given the specific requirement placed on PCGs to promote public health. The period of the project was a time of massive change and uncertainty. This report therefore tells an unfolding story of immediate threats and opportunities posed to emerging PCGs, as well as thinking about possibilities for their longer-term role in community health improvement and tackling inequalities.

The project approach

The project was based on a developmental approach. It employed a range of different methods designed to support development locally in diverse contexts, as well as to learn about common issues and mechanisms relevant to the development of national policy.

The approach was underpinned by the concept that strategy development and health improvement should be a participative and collaborative process between different players in the system. Consequently, relationships between key players – their quality, how they are built, nurtured and managed, are critical to success. Furthermore, these relationships, and the need to engage in a co-operative enterprise, should govern organisational design and development. The relationship between the lead GPs and the health authority was identified as the principal focus for the project. However, as the project progressed, this focus was extended to encompass issues relating to relationships with local authorities, a wider range of professionals working in primary care, as well as links to communities.

The project involved working with a network of twelve local partners ('sites'). Each comprised a 'team' of a representative of the health authority and a primary care organisation (emergent PCG). This network reflected the wide diversity of local contexts: location (north/south; and urban, suburban, rural); and type of primary care organisations. These emerging PCGs had different histories and experiences of involvement in primary care-led commissioning and development, including Total Purchasing Pilots, GP commissioning, 1997 NHS (Primary Care) Act Pilots and locality commissioning.

The project involved the following stages and methods that will be detailed more fully in Chapters 2 and 3.

- Taking stock of current approaches to health strategy development and the quality of relationships between the health authority and primary care, based on a structured questionnaire survey and relationship audit.
- Advisory contributions from the NHS Executive, and an external researcher with recent experience in reviewing public health approaches in primary care.
- Local developmental workshops in six sites to feed back and discuss findings, and also explore early plans for developing Health Improvement Programmes, the involvement of PCOs in the process, and opportunities for PCOs to promote public health. These in the main involved a range of health authority and NHS trust managers and primary care professionals.
- More detailed case studies of six sites.
- Network meetings of the twelve sites (the 'steering group') to feed back findings, progress and determine subsequent stages of the project.
- Testing of project findings, materials and development tools at a range of national (two university-based multi-district workshops) and local workshops.
- A scenario workshop of representatives from the twelve sites to test different future 'models' of PCGs and their public health role set in contrasting local health systems.

The context

Conceptual frameworks and perspectives

The scientific evidence, documented in the Acheson Inquiry into Inequalities in Health, supports a 'socioeconomic' model of health (Department of Health, 1998c). This model acknowledges the influence of a complex mix of factors on health. Specifically,

> 'Individual lifestyles are embedded in social and community networks and in living and working conditions, which in turn are related to the wider cultural and socioeconomic environment . . . Socioeconomic inequalities in health reflect differential exposure – from before birth and across the lifespan – to risk associated with socioeconomic position.'
> (Department of Health, 1998c, p. 8)

Consequently, improvements in health and reductions of inequalities require multi-sectoral action at national and local levels. Policies need to be both 'upstream' and 'downstream'. Maximum health benefits can only be secured if individually-oriented preventive programmes are undertaken within the context of broader measures to strengthen social networks and wider policies concerned with income distribution, education, community safety, housing, employment, transport and pollution.

The development of the public health role of primary care can be viewed within this framework, although traditionally primary care has been positioned within a narrower medical model of health. The recent trends towards a potentially more population-based focus is mapped in the figure.

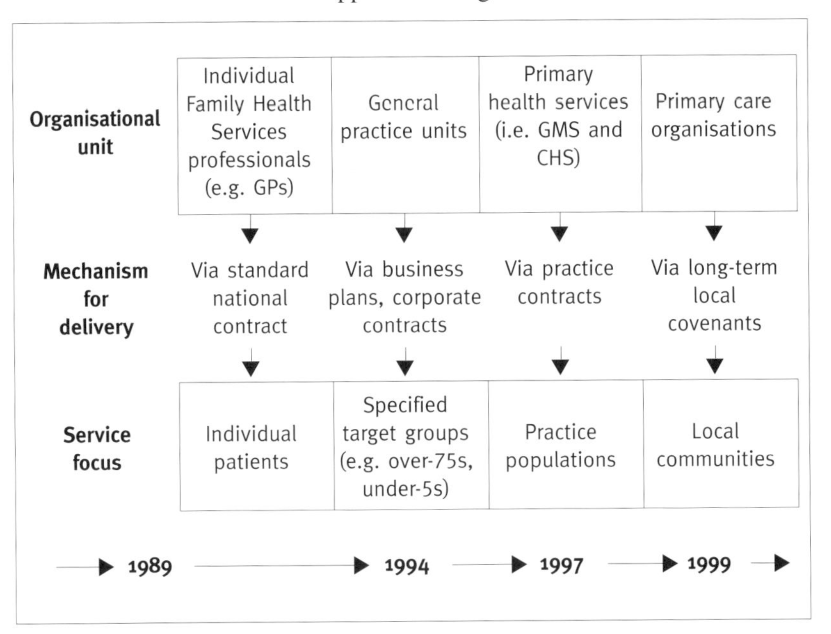

Primary health care: the direction of travel

'The rules of engagement are primary health care'
(GP chair of PCG)

The 1990–2000 period began with new national contracts for general medical (and dental) practitioners and ends with the advent of primary care trusts. The figure shows how within ten years the focus has shifted from essentially individual to community relationships in UK primary care, with specific health-care target groups and then the practice population serving as staging posts along the way. And as the relational focus has altered so too, of course, has the unit of primary care itself: from the individual Family Health Services professional contractor to the general practice and then to the multidisciplinary grouping of a primary care organisation, that now fully incorporates community health services personnel. The 1997 NHS (Primary Care) Act, for the first time, formally defined the latter as part of primary care and paved the way for future arrangements, whereby the local primary care organisation will directly control over eighty per cent of NHS resources for its area and combine both the functions of health-care provision with those of commissioning for health. In policy terms 1990–2000 represents a decade when reform has become revolution.

In practice, of course, the progression has been anything but linear. Within every district, and across many districts, the traditional model of the small primary care unit, led almost exclusively by the individual GP still pervades. Nationwide, there has been an ever-growing diversity of organisational models in primary care at practice and inter-practice level; many stimulated by the 1991–1998 fundholding experiment, and the alternative schemes it spawned. The result is that policy and organisational developments are now seeking to respond to, and incorporate, three distinct strands of primary care development.

The first is that of GP-based primary medical care: clinically oriented, personalised and generalist health care expressed through the registered list and the traditional surgery consulting room.

The second is that of the World Health Organization (WHO) derived primary health care: preventive, intersectoral and multi-professional collaboration for population health improvements; increasingly driven by European and national-level policies for targeted public health gains (WHO, 1978).

The third strand, and the most powerful, is that of primary managed care: the fusion of modern general management responsibilities with the GP professional, in whom the public has the greatest demonstrable confidence; to influence local NHS and associated resources, including decisions regarding relative clinical priorities and differential financial allocations.

It is the interplay of these three dimensions that will be important in influencing how community health improvement is secured through primary care. The extent to which the WHO definition of primary care underpins developments will be critical (Public Health Alliance, 1998). Collaboration, equity and community participation need to be central to policies, the development of new forms of organisations, programmes and services if primary care is to promote the health of communities. These components are now enshrined within the new policy framework.

'Practices have not seen public health as their business'
(community trust manager)

The new policy context

Our healthier nation acknowledges the influence of wider social, economic and environmental factors on health, and that health improvement demands action at national and local levels across a range of sectors and government policies (Department of Health, 1998a). It adopts a 'socio-economic' model of health. It aims to tackle the root causes of ill health and break the cycle of deprivation and social exclusion in order:

- To improve the health of the population as a whole by increasing the length of people's lives and the number of years spent free from illness
- To improve the health of the worst off and to narrow the health gap.

The respective roles and responsibilities of different players at national and local levels are defined in a 'national contract' for health improvement. Four national priority areas are to be addressed: heart disease and stroke, accidents, cancer and mental health. Emphasis is given to multi-agency partnerships and community participation and working in 'settings' to focus action on health in schools, workplaces and neighbourhoods.

The new NHS and *Modern local government* provide the vision of a future local collaborative 'health' system geared to improving health as well as health services (Department of Health, 1998b; Department of Environment, Transport and Regions, 1998). Health Improvement Programmes (HImPs) will be the key vehicle for implementing *Our healthier nation* and securing improvements in the four national priority areas as well as responding to local priorities. The approach to HImPs is underpinned by partnership working and new statutory duties on health bodies (including PCGs) and local authorities to work together to improve the health and wellbeing of communities. The new NHS performance framework includes health improvement indicators that monitor variations in health outcomes and risk factors of different population groups and geographical areas. Indicators will also monitor fairness of access of different groups, such as ethnic minorities, to services.

Twenty-six Health Action Zones in areas suffering the worst health record are expected to tackle inequalities in health through pioneering new forms of partnership working. Healthy Living Centres are to be the focus for inter-agency action for community health improvement at a local level. There are opportunities to link efforts to improve health with the many other government initiatives designed to bring about community regeneration. These cover economic development and employment, housing, education, and, through *Bringing Britain together: a national strategy for neighbourhood renewal*, target the needs of deprived communities and socially excluded groups (Social Exclusion Unit, 1998).

Primary care groups: delivering the agenda sets out the PCGs' health improvement role (Department of Health, 1998d). From April 1999 all PCGs were expected to improve the health of, and address health inequalities in, their community. This will involve:

- Contributing to the development of the local Health Improvement Programme and Health Action Zone plans
- Assessing health needs which will be reflected in their primary care investment plans and their contribution to the local HImP
- Direct responses to community health problems based on collaboration with other organisations, and drawing on existing public health and health promotion skills. Various examples of possible responses are shown in the box opposite
- Securing equitable access to, and quality of, primary care services for communities through primary care investment plans
- Considering use of the flexibilities provided by personal medical services pilot projects to develop services that respond in new ways to the health needs of vulnerable groups and deprived communities
- Delivering quality standards through new National Service Frameworks that cover health promotion, disease prevention, diagnosis, treatment, rehabilitation and care; with coronary heart disease and mental health representing early frameworks to be applied
- Commissioning patient services and managing new developments that are targeted on local health needs, based on evidence of clinical and cost-effectiveness, and produce an optimal balance between primary, community and secondary care services
- Providing opportunities for primary care practitioners to work with public health practitioners (health visitors, health promotion specialists, community workers); as well as health authority public health staff and others to undertake needs assessment, inter-agency work on public health issues,

Examples of PCGs' role in improving the health of their communities

- Ensuring those in greatest need are given special attention by, for example, working with local authorities and other agencies to help drug and alcohol misusers so that they are in a position to gain employment and face up to their addiction problems.
- Working with local housing departments to reduce falls in the elderly or with local schools to reduce smoking and drug use.
- Using community development approaches to improve the health of people who have difficulties accessing health care in some housing estates.
- Making services more responsive to needs such as ensuring better services for vulnerable people such as older people or children in care.
- Providing, in their one-to-one consultations with patients, health promotion and prevention interventions (e.g. smoking cessation and lifestyle advice) which can be extended by working to develop other local service initiatives such as Healthy Living Centres.

Source: Department of Health (1998d)

health promotion and disease prevention and community development work
- Being accountable through the annual review process for contributing to health improvement targets.

This is designed as a ten-year agenda of change. Change is intended to be evolutionary not revolutionary. Addressing the wider public health is perhaps the most challenging role for PCGs, given the major organisational, professional and cultural changes required.

The experience of primary care in promoting public health: the reality of the challenge

While the new policy context moves public health centre stage and provides significant opportunities for health improvement within primary care, past experience indicates the scale of challenge.

The review of the previous national health strategy, *The health of the nation – a policy assessed*, showed that:

> 'The HoN did not significantly impact upon primary care practitioners either as commissioners or providers.'

> 'The HoN was seen by those in primary as "someone else's agenda" and as irrelevant because of its population focus, long timescales and emphasis on non-medical interventions – all features which were opposite in character to the traditional GP practice.' (Department of Health, 1998e)

There is a long history and tradition of prevention and health promotion within primary care, stemming from the early community-based public health programmes (such as health visiting, community nursing and services), and preventive work in general practice. But the realisation of their full potential has often been hampered by various organisational; professional and cultural divides; the comparative underdevelopment of the scientific knowledge base; as well as the status of being the 'poor relation' within the health service.

> *'Ask what your needs are, not what are the health needs'* (community trust manager on PCG current mindsets)

Since 1990 the GP contract has provided incentives for the development of general practice-based health promotion and disease prevention and led to expansion in these services (Le Touze and Calnan, 1996). These arrangements have broadened in scope and flexibility beyond the initial narrow focus on health promotion clinics. However, various features of the scheme have remained questionable. Programmes have failed to target those most at risk of ill health or fully apply the scientific evidence (Gillam, McCartney and Thorogood, 1996; Bardsley *et al.*, 1997). For example, claims by GPs are highest in the least deprived and lowest in the most deprived areas. There are also difficulties relating to monitoring and accountability (Baeza and Calnan, 1998).

The so-called 'inverse prevention law' has operated for the full range of prevention services not just health promotion schemes (including cancer screening programmes and immunisation). Communities most at risk of ill health tend to experience the least satisfactory access to prevention services. The Acheson Inquiry into Inequalities in Health drew attention to these inequities. They are demonstrated through sub-regional and small area analyses in such areas as Liverpool and Birmingham (Flynn and Knight, 1998; Birmingham Health Authority, 1995). Nationally there is a significant mismatch between levels of need in the

Developing a public health approach in primary care

Barriers to progress

- No easily agreed definition of public health, primary care, community or locality. Primary care generally perceived as primary medical care leading to emphasis on health as an individual concern rather than a community issue.
- Primary care and public health practitioners acknowledge inequity contributes to ill health but lack confidence to address this.
- Genuine participation by local people in health viewed as helpful but problematic to achieve.
- Short-term funding and inappropriate timescales unhelpful. Good relationships and an understanding of communities take time to develop.
- Disease-focused outcome measures may take years to become significant; hinder innovations that seek to improve overall health and wellbeing rather than a specific disease process.

Enabling factors

- Committed individuals important to success of project, but often lack sustainable organisational support.
- Project workers provide bridging role in enabling local people to link with professionals in primary care.
- A geographically-based 'neutral venue' helpful for professional and lay people to meet and enable community health activities.
- Control over resources (funding, professional and personal skills).
- Supportive organisational strategies, such as jointly funded posts, imaginative and facilitative management and established corporate structures.

Source: Public Health Alliance (1998)

distribution of general practitioners as well as other primary care staff (Benzeval and Judge, 1996; Hirst, Lunt and Atkin, 1998). The pace at which the new needs-based resource allocation process enables such inequalities to be addressed will be critical to strengthening the public health base in primary care.

A recent review of public health approaches in primary care highlighted those factors, which hampered the development of more community-oriented activities and services. It also identified those factors that had proved important in supporting their development (shown in the above box).

It was only in 1996 that new health authorities were created through mergers with Family Health Services Authorities and became responsible for both primary care and commissioning other health care. The review of *The health of the nation* indicated that the development of health authorities' own organisational capacity for promoting public health had been hampered by the nature and demands of the internal market. Relationships between public health departments and primary care was an area that needed to be improved.

> *'Public health departments just work on the high cost/low volume'*
> (HA director of public health)

The evolution of different models of primary care-led commissioning (locality commissioning, fundholding and total purchasing) provide a substantial base on which to build PCGs, but the evidence suggests that organisational capabilities for promoting public health are under-developed. Such models did not lead overall to a more population-based perspective for the development of services, or for improving the health of the wider community, beyond a minority of progressive examples. Locality-based commissioning or district-wide collaborations, often with the health authority playing a key role, appear to have been more likely to develop health needs assessment capacity than multi-funds and standard fund-holding consortia (Smith, Shapiro and Ham, 1997). The findings from the national evaluation of Total Purchasing Pilots showed that total purchasing had proved to be a GP-led model of commissioning (Killoran *et al.*, 1999). Assessment of population-based needs remained largely undeveloped, although some projects piloted productive collaborative arrangements with public health departments and specialists. The evaluation also highlighted the need for PCGs to develop new ways of genuinely involving community nurses and other professionals, and working jointly with local authorities and other agencies, to prioritise and invest resources effectively to improve health as well as health care. An extensive national consultation exercise conducted by the NHS Executive revealed similar messages. The cultural, organisational and managerial challenges facing primary care with respect to public health and strategy development cannot be underestimated (Marks and Hunter, 1998).

It is clear that new robust multi-practice organisations with a public health perspective and capabilities need to be built if community health improvements are to be achieved and equity is to become reality. This will need to be viewed within the context of a long-term journey for the strategic development of primary care.

'Public health cannot be an add-on. It must be integral to the strategic development of primary care.'

The structure of the report

The chapters that follow represent the first stages in this journey. Chapter 2 sets out where primary care and health authority staff are both in their understanding of health strategy and of each other. Despite drawing on the views of those at the local leading edge, it shows just how far there is to go. At local levels there are few health strategies worth the title, and relationships are overwhelmingly operational, not strategic. Chapter 2 is the downside. Chapter 3 is more upbeat, indicating the real potential for health partnerships that exists in the English health system, once it releases itself from the shackles of the old NHS. The organisational developments emerging for primary health care are described and analysed. Their fragility is self-evident; and accordingly the report concludes with a final chapter setting out some of the key policy issues that require attention over the next two years to ensure that these developments are nurtured and sustained. Between the chapters and in Appendix C are detailed district case materials illustrating the emergent good practice, as new primary care organisations seek to achieve a successful balance between the effective delivery of health care and their new public health responsibilities.

'Net winners or net losers – it's in the balance'
(HA director of primary care)

References

Baeza, J and Calnan, M (1998). Beating the bands? *Health Service Journal*, **109**(5623): 26–7.

Bardsley, M, Bevan, P, Gill, M and Jacobson, B (1997). *Health in the capital: a city-wide perspective.* London: The Health of Londoners' Project.

Benzeval, M and Judge, K (1996). Access to healthcare in England: continuing inequalities in the distribution of general practitioners. *Journal of Public Health Medicine* **18**: 33–40.

Birmingham Health Authority (1995). *Birmingham annual public health report: closing the gap.* Birmingham: Birmingham Health Authority.

Department of Environment, Transport and Regions (1998). *Modern local government: in touch with the people.* London: Stationery Office.

Department of Health (1998a). *Our healthier nation: a contract for health.* London: Stationery Office.

Department of Health (1998b). *The new NHS: modern. Dependable.* London: Stationery Office.

Department of Health (1998c). *Independent Inquiry into Inequalities in Health: Report* [Acheson Report]. London: Stationery Office.

Department of Health (1998d). *Primary care groups: delivering the agenda.* HSC 1998/228: LAC (98) 32.

Department of Health (1998e). *The health of the nation : a policy assessed.* London: Stationery Office.

Flynn, P and Knight, D (1998). *Inequalities in health in the North West.* Warrington: NHS Executive, North West.

Gillam, S, McCartney, P and Thorogood, M (1996). *British Medical Journal* **312**: 324–5.

Hirst, M, Lunt, N and Atkin, K (1998). Were practice nurses equitably distributed across England and Wales 1988–1995? *Journal of Health Services Research and Policy* **3**: 31–8.

Killoran, A, Mays, N, Wyke, S and Mallson, G (1999). *Total purchasing: a step towards primary care groups.* London: King's Fund.

Le Touze, S and Calnan, M (1996). The banding scheme for health promotion in general practice. *Health Trends* **28**: 100–5.

Marks, L and Hunter, D (1998). *The development of primary care groups: policy into practice.* Birmingham: NHS Executive.

Public Health Alliance (1998). *Beyond Acheson: an agenda for the new public health.* Birmingham: Public Health Alliance.

Smith, J, Shapiro, J and Ham, C (1997). *Mapping approaches to commissioning: extending the mosaic*. Birmingham: Health Services Management Centre, University of Birmingham.

Social Exclusion Unit (1998). *Bringing Britain together: a national strategy for urban renewal.* London: Stationery Office.

World Health Organization and the United Nations Children's Fund (1978). *The Alma-Ata Declaration.* Geneva: WHO and UNICEF.

Local case study: Nottingham

Context

Nottingham Health Authority has established six primary care groups (PCGs). These are coterminous in the main with the three district councils, and there are three PCGs within the new Nottingham unitary local authority. The groups range in size from 85,000 to 128,000 population.

The development of the HImP has involved cross-health authority workshops involving all stakeholders including GPs nominated by the local medical committee (LMC) prior to shadow PCGs. The programme has three strands each led by a strategic forum: health, NHS services and jointly commissioned services. A reference group ensures integration of the strands and that underpinning themes are addressed. The Greater Nottingham Partnership Forum Executive, an independent body comprising council leaders, local authority chief executives, health authority, business and voluntary body representatives, will 'sign off' the HImP. PCGs are expected to participate in this structure.

PCGs are to initially operate at level 2 as a sub-committee of the health authority with delegated budgets for hospital and community health services (HCHS) (except for specialist services), GMS cash-limited and prescribing. A pan-Nottingham Commissioning Group consisting of PCG representatives will collectively commission secondary care.

The development of the public health role of PCGs is planned to involve:

- *Contributing to the HAZ*, which will focus on inequalities, particularly families. The HAZ director will work with a HAZ implementation post in each PCG. This post will be a secondment of a professional/ clinical person working within the PCG.
- *Developing public health skills* through 'outreach' support provided by the public health department on health profiling and local health action; enhancement of the skills of PCG staff, for example through GP attachments to the public health department; development of the research capability of PCGs in conjunction with the university; and in multidisciplinary audit, including areas of chronic disease and prevention.
- *Targets and performance management.* PCGs will be encouraged to develop their own local health plans defining their contribution to Nottingham targets. PCGs will develop their 'own way', working closely with the community. Lay members have been appointed to the PCG boards and include local councillors and people with voluntary and community development backgrounds, with the aim of developing community development approaches.
- *Contributing to the HImP.* PCGs will continue to be active partners in developing the HImP, which it is anticipated will become increasingly public health-focused over time.

One PCG's perspective

The PCG (incorporating the previous Primary Care Act Pilot – 'PRIME') is planning to select the national target area of coronary heart disease (CHD) and also substance misuse and homelessness as local priority issues. Local priorities should 'represent areas that are of major importance to people's everyday life'. Information has shown that the population has lower access to services for CHD, and a more proactive approach is required, which is likely to be based on a nurse-led community-oriented way of working, targeting those most at risk.

The PCG will be able to build on the experience of the Primary Care Act Pilot. Learning points have included:

- Every practice must be represented on the board and nursing representation is essential, particularly to avoid medical domination.
- The health authority and community trust should be co-opted to the board to ensure a co-operative approach.
- Effective 'lay' input must involve a more sophisticated approach. Board members will meet democratic representatives of the communities based on the structure established by the City Council to discuss and define their perception of needs, and ideas to feed into the PCG.

The PRIME project illustrates the type of community-based action that is envisaged in other PCGs. The project has developed a range of community-based initiatives and relationships which will support the PCG's future public health role. This includes the HEALS (Healthy Living in Sneinton and St Anns) project. Ten practices are linked to fifteen local schools to develop health promotion, specifically incorporating health promotion within the curriculum, with priorities chosen by children and parents. It has involved collaboration with the community trust health promotion department; school nurses linking with practices; and designated lead teachers and parents and children. An initiative to reduce accidents is being undertaken in partnership with the City Council housing department, as well as Age Concern and local schools. Such health promotion initiatives have been developed through funding from a variety of sources including City Council grants and are co-ordinated by a needs assessment postholder appointed through savings from Fundholding.

Barriers

- Time demands of engaging in the process of restructuring service provision
- Difficulties in forming multi-disciplinary teams that support and encourage the involvement of key personnel including nursing staff
- Lack of skills and training in the areas of public health and health improvement. Most board members have little idea and experience of the possibilities of the public health role of PCGs and their learning needs will need to be addressed
- The difference in culture between the public health department and primary care; and specifically the culture of general practice – the need to shift from the individual patient to the collective population perspective
- The board will not necessarily be representative of primary care or the community, and therefore ways of securing wider effective representation and inputs are required
- The management funding available to PCGs may not be sufficient
- Decisions about how much of the budget should be available for the development of primary and community services and how much should be blocked back for secondary care will be difficult
- The health authority may be reluctant to let go – reduce its power – while it is still held accountable for PCG decisions
- The extent to which trusts contribute and adhere to the HImP and enable shifts in resources is still to be tested.

Critical success factors

- Potential of 'seeing the benefits for all', particularly with respect to inequalities; need to find 'low hanging fruit' areas for early action where benefits for practices are possible
- Mobilising the health community to work more closely with local government so the community is involved
- Moving from a practice/doctor-centred view to a team/corporate population view.

(November 1998)

2. Engagement: primary care and the public health agenda

This chapter reports the findings from the first stage of the project. This focused on exploring and supporting project participants' engagement with the new public health agenda. It involved assessing the extent to which current approaches to involving primary care in the development of health strategies 'fit' with the notion of a more 'partnership' approach to the development of Health Improvement Programmes, that respond to local community needs as well as nationally defined priorities and health targets. It included an assessment of the nature and quality of the underpinning relationships between primary care organisations and health authorities over the issues of promoting public health. The focus was often initially on the links between the professional functions of public health medicine and general practice, as there was an immediate need to harness and develop the potential contribution of this relationship as the starting point to establishing wider partnerships around strategic issues. Indeed, many of the project participants were clear that getting these relationships right would be crucial to further developing joint working around Health Improvement Programmes and action plans.

Practically, it involved undertaking a survey of approaches to health strategy development and a relationship audit, and feeding back the findings through local visits. This combination of methods was employed as the project's overall approach, as set out in Chapter 1, was based on the view that strategy development and health improvement must be a participative and collaborative process between different players in the system. The nature and quality of relationships are therefore critical.

PCGs are not *de novo* creations. Their diverse nature and development experience are significantly influenced by the legacy of how previous policies have been implemented as well as by a diverse range of specific local contextual factors. These include the nature of the local community, its health status, organisational boundaries, political structures and dynamics, relationships with other NHS and non-NHS organisations, and the particular individuals involved. PCGs' capacity to improve public health as well as deliver health care will depend on the extent to which these legacies can either be built on or overcome. This stage was about helping project participants review the legacies of their local processes, relationships and contexts as the basis for addressing the new public health agenda.

The first part of this chapter summarises the findings of the survey of approaches to health strategy development. The second part describes the results of the relationship audit. It concludes with some of the early overall learning from these exercises.

Developing a strategic approach to health improvement

It is important to note that, at this stage in the project, *Our healthier nation* was still on the drawing board. The Green Paper (Department of Health, 1998a) which heralded the beginning of the consultation process was not published until some six months after the project began, in February 1998.

Nevertheless, there had *been* a national strategy for health in place for the past five years, and evidence from local work (including an evaluation of the implementation of Health of the Nation in North Thames, undertaken by the South East Institute of Public Health), suggested that some progress had been made on the health improvement agenda. However, this progress was known to be patchy, with primary care involvement in the health strategy process understood to be particularly limited, as illustrated by the following comment:

> *'. . . overall, the HoN had minimal impact on GP practices. One GP said that there was "no connection (locally) between HoN and primary care in any meaningful way . . ."'*
> (Department of Health, 1998b)

Health authority (public health) response	Primary care-led response
'Written health strategy – developed in 1994 . . . key health programme areas developed based on programme budgeting'	'Formal existing health strategy is owned by health authority. Primary care feels very little ownership of this . . . Primary care group are currently exploring strategic ways of solving key areas of health needs perceived by primary care workers. There is still very little "public" involvement in strategy formulation.'
'The annual report of the DPH is the core document, together with the HA overall commissioning plan. There is no "bespoke" strategy . . . a small needs assessment project . . . in 1996 provided some strategic direction . . . '	'The health authority has a substantial plan . . . published September 1995. We don't feel any particular ownership of it, and it does not address our local issues.'
'We have a five-year strategy for health and health services. It focuses very much on intersectoral working. There are various feeder strategies, e.g. child plan, a primary care strategy. DPH reports are topic based. We have a primary/community care strategy.'	'We have requested the health authority to prioritise a partnership with our steering group over the next year to define all aspects of contributing to our localities' health needs profile.'

Taking stock of local strategies – the method

The initial stock-take of the current strategies took the form of a postal survey, using a framework designed for the project, which built on the work undertaken by the South East Institute of Public Health for the *Health of the nation* evaluation. Participants from public health and primary care were asked to complete the survey separately, and to return it to the project team for analysis. Issues arising from the analysis of responses then formed the basis for further discussion in the local developmental workshops.

The survey asked a number of 'retrospective' questions about:

- current strategies to improve health, and the form these took
- key priorities/target areas, what these were based on and how they had been agreed
- what lessons had been learnt from the process.

It then went on to ask a number of questions which required participants to think ahead to:

- how these local strategies and priorities might change in response to *Our healthier nation* and the process of developing a local Health Improvement Programme
- how each organisation would approach joint working on *Our healthier nation*
- what kind of support PCGs or health authorities might need to support the development and implementation of HImPs, and where this might be available
- what resources were available to support this – within and beyond the health authority.

Finally, participants were asked to identify how primary care organisations would be able to influence the setting of local priorities and targets (see Appendix A).

Taking stock of local strategies – the issues

One of the clearest messages to emerge was that everyone was at different starting points. There was great variation between health authorities, and between primary care organisations – in their approaches to strategy; in their understanding of the health improvement agenda; in the processes by which they agreed priorities; and their experience of the process. This is illustrated by comparing some paired responses (see table above).

(i) Current strategy – comparing health authority and primary care approaches

A number of key issues were evident from these initial responses, including:

- the discrepancy between the health authority and primary care descriptions of their current position in relation to health strategy
- the obvious lack of ownership of health authority strategies in primary care

Health authority priorities	Primary care priorities
Public information and education Develop workforce plans Longer-term agreements Improve skills for prioritisation	'Involve providers, carers, voluntary/statutory agencies . . . in decisions concerning provision of primary care.'
Elderly Children Mental health Tertiary services Diabetes Asthma	'Keeping waiting times generally low for acute community and mental health services . . . '
CHD/stroke Mental health Injury/accidents Cancer Infection and internal disease Pregnancy and the newborn Generic health programmes	Anxiety/depression – counselling services Orthopaedics/backs – local back pain service Drug and alcohol misuse – specialist worker Stroke – community stroke programme

- 'strategies for health' clearly carried different meanings for different organisations.

These issues were further explored in the local workshops, where it soon became evident that health authority responses were often in fact describing service development strategies or local purchasing plans, rather than broader approaches to improve health through multi-agency approaches. Some primary care organisations, on the other hand, described their practice development or business plans. The differences offered a rich source for enquiry.

(ii) Priorities

Participants were also asked to list their key priorities or targets, and to give further information on the processes and mechanisms on which these were based. Many of these priorities were service-focused, as well as issues concerned with organisational development. Some illustrative examples are listed in the table above.

Overall, priorities seemed to be based on a mixture of issues, which can broadly be categorised as

- disease-based
- client group-based
- service development
- organisational development.

(iii) How were these priorities decided?

These priorities had been arrived at through a number of approaches, which seemed to reflect local organisational history rather more than local health needs. *Health of the nation*, population-based needs assessment, practice information, professional anecdotes and stakeholder workshops were all cited, though only a minority of responses included the five *Health of the nation* key areas. One pair of participants (North and Mid-Hampshire Health Authority/ Blackwater Valley Primary Care Group) were hoping to build on a local Health for All partnership to inform their Health Improvement Programme.

Health authorities talked about having taken 'a broad, partnership approach' to priority-setting but, on closer investigation, this was often limited to brief consultation with local social services departments, or 'multidisciplinary' approaches 'informed mostly by health professionals.' Primary care organisations, on the other hand, admitted to 'GP anecdote and day-to-day experience', or 'discussion with colleagues in GP practices' as well as 'feedback from providers about specific pressures their staff are experiencing.'

The priority-setting process seemed to fall into two broad approaches, with various degrees of 'inclusiveness' – ranging from sending out a strategy for consultation, to involving all key stakeholders in a series of local priority-setting workshops.

Health authority (public health)	Primary care
' . . . involving more players earlier to gain ownership'	'We haven't got a strategy!'
' . . . national imperatives re waiting lists and efficiency have overridden strategic priorities'	'We need to incorporate views of local people and local non-health organisations.'
'Implementation of OHN is a fundamental element of the HImP.'	'We need commitment from all participants about the overall view, the specific priorities within it and who's going to do what to address them.'
'Steep learning curve for all concerned; no one strategy can satisfy everyone.'	'We need to set ourselves actual targets for health, and find ways to measure their achievement (rather than listing services which we all provide).'
'Implementation: difficult to make the strategy real or keep it fresh in people's minds.'	'We need commitment to action by local organisations and individuals to help achieve targets for improved health.'

Reactive prioritisation

One health authority summed up this more reactive (or pragmatic) approach by stating:

'Prioritisation was informed by national pressures, local pressures from service providers and users . . . therefore pressures dictated how agreement was reached.'

These pressures did not always come from within the NHS. As another health authority told us:

'Social services budgetary constraints and high spend helped push community care issues high up the list.'

Some organisations had, however, taken a more proactive approach to prioritisation, with local stakeholder workshops and forums which included a wide number of local organisations.

Proactive prioritisation

'a seminar of stakeholder days was held, including specific priority-setting workshops'

'a chief executives' forum exists which was a key driver. Consultation took place widely, including the CHC, black and ethnic minority groups, the voluntary sector. Sixty-plus organisations were offered presentations/discussion – not just paper.'

What had people learnt from developing local health strategies?

Clearly, a number of important lessons had been learnt from the experience of developing strategies and agreeing priorities, and the task of having to complete the framework began to open up a debate about these issues. This debate was further developed within the local workshops. Again, some illustrative responses are given above.

There was a clear feeling that strategy needed to be 'made real' and to be kept fresh in people's minds: 'It's a steep learning curve for all concerned; no one strategy can satisfy everyone.' Strategy development and implementation was beginning to be seen as an iterative process, with learning for individuals and organisations needing to be built in at all stages.

Moving forward

How did health authority and primary care participants think their strategies and priorities would change in response to *Our healthier nation* and the development of local Health Improvement Programmes?

Again, there was a range of responses, with some feeling 'it fits with our broad direction of travel' whilst others foresaw current strategies and priorities being 'potentially subject to significant change.' However, there was broad agreement on the need for local solutions, and local commitment:

'Whatever we produce needs to be in local terms, which local people and organisations can relate to and which addresses our specific issues' *(GP consortium member)*

Mechanisms for achieving this were much less clear, and in most cases either underdeveloped or based on various ad hoc arrangements. 'We're only at the start of the consultation process, and agreement of the timetable for progress' (HA); and 'We don't know, although we are willing to make ourselves available for consultation' (GP consortia), were typical responses on being asked about the approaches to working in partnership on *Our healthier nation*. One emerging PCG summed this up:

'This is not yet clear. Initially, there is work to be done in simply facilitating introductions, and explaining ideas. Through educational initiatives, GPs and PCOs could have [their] knowledge base improved about multi-agency working for public health. Public health physicians and HFA coordinators [are] key players in this, together with Health Promotion.' (PCG chair)

Supporting effective strategy development and implementation

All participants were asked what support they felt they would need to take this agenda forward, and what resources were currently available to them. Both health authority and primary care respondents said they needed to further develop their

- public health skills and knowledge
- information sources
- research evidence.

Mechanisms for doing this included

- organisational development
- education and training
- personal and professional development.

More specifically, people from both organisations stressed the need to take a local view of health needs and interventions to improve health; and the need to translate strategic objectives into local action.

Support needed to make an effective contribution to health improvement

'Looking at the determinants of health at a locality level will be crucial in order to be able to measure impact' (assistant director of commissioning in a health authority)

'Support will be needed in the process of determining priorities . . . this will require meaningful information from public health and primary care. Similar support [will be] required in turning priorities into action – we need to be able to demonstrate outcomes.' (health authority manager)

'The focus needs to move to implementation, not just development of strategy.' (HA director of primary care)

'Help in community development, community participation and ownership' (GP)

Resources to support this work were generally felt to be widely available, within and beyond the local public health department – although these were not always perceived to be being used to maximum effect at the time of the survey. Health authorities in particular felt these resources were 'available, but already very stretched.'

Some emerging primary care groups felt the need to develop 'in-house' skills and expertise, though they were aware of the need for economies of scale:

'We would like to reach a point where we have most of the skills needed within our own PCG, to maintain and implement the HImP, but with reasonable access to specialist skills/experience as required.' (GP consortium chair)

Others were more circumspect:

'PCGs will need to know what public health knowledge they require, but do not need to have the skills themselves. It is important that people with different skills are able to collaborate, rather than try and teach one group new skills.' (PCG manager)

This emphasis on the need to develop multi-disciplinary and multi-professional approaches to the development and implementation of health strategy, both within the health authority and in primary care, was widespread. Public health skills and expertise were *not* seen as being located solely within the profession of public health medicine.

Participants from both health authorities and primary care organisations cited the wealth of public health resources available in local authorities, trusts, primary care teams, health promotion departments and other organisations, though all felt that this was difficult to access and to engage. Others talked of existing links with academic departments. Most stressed the need for a multidisciplinary approach to public health.

One participant summarised this succinctly:

> 'The public health function in the health authority is wider than simply public health physicians. Team/patch working will aid the multi-professional approach, and include health promotion staff and health visitors employed by trusts . . . ' (HA consultant in public health)

Resources currently available to support this work

'Health for All coordinators exist in all four local authority areas. Their role can be capitalised in this respect.'

'Essentially, the resources . . . are available across a range of organisations . . . the problem is accessing and coordinating these resources to support development and implementation of this strategy.'

'Other organisations need to be engaged and coordinated appropriately.'

'The challenge is in engaging practices (GPs) in the process . . . '

'Underestimated resource is that of enthusiasm. If key people can become engaged in the process, and signs of early success can be seen, then momentum can be created and sustained that drives the initial change. Sustainability then becomes an issue because, unless the process becomes properly resourced, and therefore efforts are appreciated, involvement may dwindle to the enthusiastic few, which is not sustainable.'

How influential will the new primary care groups be in future?

At the time of the survey, both public health and primary care participants felt optimistic that the new primary care organisations would be able to influence the health improvement agenda: 'Once they are properly organised, the PCGs will be well placed to determine local needs and to contribute to the setting of priorities and targets' (consultant in public health); 'People will have a direct voice' (HA assistant director of commissioning); 'PCGs will influence through joint knowledge and experience, and through changing patients' and colleagues' perspectives' (health authority director of primary care). Two further comments:

> 'GPs and nurses see the levels and impact of illness every day. They will be key players in informing others who don't have the same direct exposure as part of the overall discussion. Their experience should be supported by primary care data wherever possible.' (GP)

> 'We will press hard for a real shift of resources to where effective interventions have been shown to meet agreed need.' (PCG chair)

Primary care groups and public health: the relational challenge

The second part of this chapter now looks at the extent to which the kinds of relationship that were in place in 1998 would enable the development and implementation of health strategies that would engage PCGs and secure community health improvement.

Many organisations, agencies and individuals have a stake in improving public health: the nature and quality of the relationships between them will be a significant factor in the development of effective and appropriate Health Improvement Programmes. The link between relationship and strategy can be seen as a cycle: the process of strategy development is enabled by effective relation-ships but can also constitute a trigger for relationship development. The cycle may be virtuous or vicious: relationships, organisational development and public health strategy can be mutually reinforcing (which does not, of course, preclude encountering various crisis points), but can also become mutually destructive.

The challenge for PCGs lies in the fact that the development and delivery of a public health strategy depends upon a wide range of relationships which may be new relationships, different kinds of relationship, or previously neglected or difficult relationships.

The extent to which improving public health as well as delivering health care will involve new relationships varied among project participants, though, by virtue of their 'leading-edge' status, their relational base is possibly likely to have been more extensive and developed than average. Some PCOs, for example, had established relationships with local authorities while for others these were substantially new relationships to be created. Focused localised relationships with PCOs, such as neighbourhood nursing teams which co-incided with local authority community action forums, helped develop relationships through continuously meeting the same people as well as allowing mutual influence of agendas. These appeared more effective than relationships with health authorities which were unable to adequately resource the relationship – particularly where this was seen as requiring public health directorate time. All the PCOs had been working with other general practices to varying degrees, but all also faced the problem of developing relationships with fringe practices that were reluctant participants.

In all cases the existing relationships were seen as being liable to significant change with the establishment of PCGs. This would be in terms of the individuals involved, the structure and power basis of the relationship, in working practices or in style. The prospect of these changes created considerable uncertainty, and in some cases significant disquiet. This was partly a consequence of the uncertainty surrounding how PCG development would take place during the course of the project, but was also a reflection of deep-rooted and fundamental fears about some of the changes. These fears are likely to remain an important influence on the relationships for some time. From the GPs' perspective concerns included their relationships with patients and the possible tension between being an advocate of the individual patient as well as responsible for resource prioritisation at a population level; their relationships with other professions; and their relationships with other GPs (for example in the context of clinical governance). Fundamentally for the project the relationship between health authorities and the PCOs was also changing with sometimes divergent views on future roles and levels of influence.

The realignment of relationships with acute and community trusts was also in the background although not a focus of the project. Much of the change in these relationships surrounded the shifting sands of competition and collaboration. Under both the internal market and in the 'New NHS' competition and collaboration have co-existed and will continue to co-exist. The focus and nature of competition, and the extent of collaboration, may, however, vary significantly.

In all cases there was a legacy of difficult personal or organisational relationships. Project participants were not immune to such well-known obstacles to collaboration as:

- working practices
- organisational structures and cultures
- professional cultures and training
- misunderstanding and poor communication interests
- territorial interests and tribalism – defending power, status and influence
- funding systems
- low morale, work pressures and financial pressures
- geography and the lack of common boundaries.

The challenge of relationships for PCGs is not just a public health issue but also an organisational one. One participating GP, fearing that colleague GPs would in the end need to be bought off rather than readily buy in to the new agenda, commented that GPs regarded general practices as 'principally small businesses providing a public service, not public services run as small businesses'. Yet the small business, as indeed is any organisation, is fundamentally a relational phenomenon:

> 'The best way of characterising the world of the small business, to my mind, is that it is a world of managing sets of interdependencies on a day-to-day basis with a wide range of stakeholders (another new fashionable word in the large company management literature). These include customers, suppliers, distributors, wholesalers and middlemen, bankers, accountants, property owners, lawyers, regulatory authorities of all shapes and sizes, competitors as well as "assistance" agencies and family, friends and

staff. Paradoxically most people who start small businesses say they do it to achieve independence. In fact they are usually exchanging a well defined and stable form of dependence (in a job) for a wide range of interdependencies which they must manage carefully, in order to maintain stability, but which they cannot control.' (Gibb, 1995)

Recognising that developing and managing a wide range of internal and external relationships is an important part of any organisation's life, and not just the consequence of a particular health agenda, may help PCGs rise to the relational challenge. The world of the small business is, in fact, a good training ground for the relationship management skills which are essential for playing a full role in improving public health. It is, however, important to remember that these relationships are not ends in themselves. All organisational development must keep in mind the purpose of the organisation, a major part of which for PCGs is improving public health.

Primary care groups and public health: which relationships?

The twin relational pressures for improving public health and overall organisational effectiveness put many relationships on to the agenda. Project participants were both excited by the opportunities that these new relationships presented, but also daunted by the prospect of competing demands on many fronts. It was clear that it would be important to prioritise relationships and identify the points at which investment in different relationships was likely to be needed.

In the course of testing project materials a group of health authority staff with responsibility for PCG development were asked to identify the key relationships for PCGs at different levels, and to see how these relationship priorities would change over time. Between levels 1 and 4 there were significant differences in both the number of relationships and also the balance between internal and external relationships (see Chapter 3 for an explanation of the four levels). This also provided some guidance on where investment in relationships should be prioritised according to those which were most important, or likely to become so, and those which were currently weakest. The table opposite illustrates the additional relationships that were viewed as becoming increasingly important at different levels.

At the start of the project there was considerable uncertainty as to where health authorities should fit on the relational map. In simulations there was a tendency for level 1 PCGs to see the health authority as a key relationship, for level 3 PCGs to seek their dissolution and for level 4 PCGs to seek to reinvent them to come to their rescue. The tendency was to see the future role in terms of guarantor or regulator of relationships, but this move towards a more distant relationship did not always fit easily with the immediate responsibility for establishing PCGs and the close involvement this could bring. The very different nature of the relationship with prospective level 1 PCGs and those which were ambitious to progress rapidly to levels 3 or 4 was also difficult for health authorities to manage.

Relationship profiling: the method

Recognising that there were many relationships involved, the project took as its entry point the relationships between health authorities and PCOs. The aim was to provide an initial stocktake of this relationship and to assess the extent to which the relationship was capable of supporting the development and delivery of a public health strategy. As the focus of the project shifted to future organisational development and strategy, other relationships were increasingly brought into the discussion although they were not formally profiled.

Given the scope of the project the aim of the profiles was not so much to provide robust comparable measures of relationships but to capture current perceptions of the relationship as a focus for structured reflection about their strengths, weaknesses and development needs. Given the demanding timetable for PCG development the relationships were also a moving target: all participants found that during the course of the project some of the problems in relationships were being addressed and resolved and new pressures were emerging.

There is no simple model of a good relationship: different organisational types and responsibilities bring different relational demands. Organisational cultures and individual personalities differ greatly, again leading to different kinds of relationship. However, in developing new organisations and seeking significant organisational development, with

Key relationships now	Relationship expectations of PCGs for 2001			
	Level 1	**Level 2**	**Level 3**	**Level 4**
PCG board	GPC	Inter-practice forums (e.g. audit)	Community trust (clinicians and managers)	New primary care trusts national group
Inter-practice	Individual patients	Health authority members and chief executive	Local authorities (several departments)	NICE/CHIMP Communities
Intra-practice	Health authority managers	Hospital consultants Communities	Voluntary organisations	NHSE
Health authority	GP – practice staff	Prescribing adviser	PHC team relationships	Media and politicians
Acute trust			Client groups	Major providers Regional offices/ assemblies

consequent changes in systems, structures, work practices and professional cultures, it is important to consider the impact of these changes on the potential for effective relationships to develop. Too often relationships are left to evolve as a by-product of changes driven by other factors. Where performance measurement lacks an adequate relational dimension there is a danger that relationships will be undermanaged and even undermined by actions taken in response to the demands of other accountability frameworks.

The approach to the relationship profiling was therefore to look at the extent to which the preconditions for effective relationships were in place and being fostered. This draws on a model for relational auditing developed by the Relationships Foundation.* There are many well established psychometric approaches to looking at interpersonal or team relationships, but diagnostics to support the development of relationships between organisations are less well developed. Current approaches to social audit (see, for example, Wheeler and Sillanpaa, 1997) provide some assessment of stakeholder relationships and assurance of management focus but are not principally designed to aid their development.

The approach adopted by the Relationships Foundation is to focus on the relational environment – which include such factors as organisational structure and culture, work practices, infrastructure, and skills – and the extent to which this creates the preconditions that will foster effective relationships. It is structured around five dimensions which are regarded as necessary, but not sufficient, conditions for effective relationships. As the approach does not presuppose a particular model of a 'good' relationship the weighting attached to each dimension, and its particular focus, varies according to the kind of the relationship and the particular context.

A full relational audit operates at a number of levels: exploring beliefs about the kind of relationship that should exist; comparing expectations and experience of the relationship; and identifying and assessing causal factors influencing the relationship. Within the scope of this project the more limited objective was to capture initial perceptions of the relationship as a basis for structured discussion about the relationship. This was focused around concerns identified and differences in perception of the relationship. A questionnaire was constructed around the framework of preconditions described below. Questions which relate to each dimension, together with answers from one of the participating sites, are also shown. 'Lead' individuals on health strategy from each participating organisation were asked to fill in the profile questionnaire prior to the local workshops where these individual results were used to focus discussion with a wider group of local participants to test the emerging profile of the relationship.

*This was initially developed in the context of work for the Scottish Prison Service (Scottish Prison Service Occasional Papers, Report No. 2, 1995) and has subsequently been developed for use in the health and business sectors.

Table i – Commonality	Strongly agree	Slightly agree	Neither agree or disagree	Slightly disagree	Strongly disagree
Our understanding of health is basically the same		● ■			
We combine our different skills and perspectives to make a positive contribution to public health			●	■	
Our goals for the development of this relationship are different		● ■			
The interests of our own organisations impede partnership	● ■				
Our priorities for public health are very different		● ■			

● Health authority ■ PCO

Table ii – Parity	Strongly agree	Slightly agree	Neither agree or disagree	Slightly disagree	Strongly disagree
We both benefit from greater involvement by primary care organisations in public health	●		■		
I am treated courteously and with respect	■			●	
We respect each other's different views and contribution		● ■			
I have a say in decisions which affect my work	●	■			
Responsibility is fairly shared			■	●	

● Health authority ■ PCO

(i) Commonality – valuing similarity and difference*

Commonality enables individuals and organisations to work together towards shared goals. While tensions can be creative, and there may be differences in roles and responsibilities, if these are not set in the context of some shared objectives and understanding, then the likelihood of performance-hindering conflict may be increased.

Common objectives provide the basis for working together. Without real, shared, defined objectives (as opposed to generalised goals), organisations may end up pulling in different directions or come into conflict over priorities. The process by which agreement on objectives is reached is important in building commonality.

Shared culture reduces the risk of misunderstandings, difficulty in articulating shared objectives and the lack of a shared basis for resolving differences of opinion. This applies to both professional and organisational cultures. A sense of common identity, of ultimately being in the same boat, can reflect the strength of the relationship as well as providing a basis for its development. This may be expressed through establishing some common culture or through developing working practices which take account of different cultures rather than just working round them or simply ignoring them. Commonality does not require uniformity. Differences can add value to a relationship although it is important that they are seen as enriching the relationship and not just as obstacles to be overcome (see Table i).

(ii) Parity – the use and abuse of power

Parity does mean equality in a relationship. Authority, influence or rewards in a relationship may rightly vary, though it is important that

* This account of the framework is reproduced with permission of the Relationships Foundation.

Table iii – Multiplexity	Strongly agree	Slightly agree	Neither agree or disagree	Slightly disagree	Strongly disagree
The constraints on what I can contribute to public health are understood			●	■	
We have a good knowledge of each other as individuals			■	●	
We have an all-round picture of each other's particular work interests		■	●		

● Health authority ■ PCO

Table iv – Continuity	Strongly agree	Slightly agree	Neither agree or disagree	Slightly disagree	Strongly disagree
We are in contact often enough to maintain a good working relationship	■		●		
Not enough attention is paid to long-term issues		● ■			
We have been working together long enough to develop a good understanding	■			●	
This is a long-term relationship	● ■				
New staff are quick to pick up on the key issues		●		■	

● Health authority ■ PCO

differentials are accepted and not abused. It is rarely a simple picture, for there are many different kinds of power (financial control, regulatory authority, political influence, control of delivery, or exit and veto rights) in a relationship and different parties in a relationship are likely to have different kinds of power.

Parity requires, and is fostered by, participation and involvement which ensures that people have some real say in decisions that affect their work. Lack of participation may mean that strategic objectives are not owned, may reduce morale and stifle innovation. Inadequate influence in a relationship with respect to tasks or responsibilities is a frequent source of frustration.

The fairness of benefits in a relationship can engender co-operation and foster commitment to a relationship from which both parties can benefit. 'Win-win' relationships where the benefits are identified and clearly communicated are more likely to be successful. Fair conduct in the relationship is necessary for trust and respect. Double standards, prejudice and favouritism are extremely corrosive (see Table ii).

(iii) Multiplexity – breadth of knowledge

Multiplexity looks at the breadth of the relationship. This can enhance mutual understanding and enable a broader appreciation of the range of skills and experience that individuals or organisations can contribute.

Knowledge of a counterpart's organisation or department is important to appreciate the constraints under which they work, identify shared objectives and develop appropriate ways of joint working. Knowledge of role or skills is important for the effectiveness of joint work and helps avoid flawed assumptions or misunderstandings, missed opportunities or sub-optimal use of resources. Knowledge of the person (such as interests or values) can strengthen the relationship and aid its management (see Table iii).

(iv) Continuity – shared time over time

Time is the currency of relationships. The continuity of contact, over a period of time, provides the opportunity for both individual and

Table v – Directness	Strongly agree	Slightly agree	Neither agree or disagree	Slightly disagree	Strongly disagree
I can get in touch when I need to	■			●	
My messages and questions are responded to promptly	■		●		
I often hear about decisions which affect my work via the grapevine				●	■
We can be open with one another				● ■	
Any concerns I may have are picked up on quickly		● ■			
There are enough opportunities for us to meet face to face	■			●	

● Health authority ■ PCO

organisational relationships to develop, although difficult decisions may need to be made about which relationships to invest time in. When time is invested in a relationship is also important: time invested up front at the start of a relationship can avoid time- consuming problems downstream.

The length and stability of the relationship over time creates the opportunity for individual rapport and improved mutual understanding to develop, as well as providing a context for long-term issues to be addressed at an organisational level. Where staff turnover is high, locking in the benefits of individual and informal relationships to create an organisational history and overview of the relationship is often important. Managing change in the relationship is important if such benefits of change as career progression and the bringing in of new people are to be achieved without undermining the quality and effectiveness of existing relationships (see Table iv).

(v) Directness – the quality of the communication process

Directness influences the quality of communication in the relationship. The medium of communication affects the amount and quality of information exchanged. Face-to-face communication, for example, allows non-verbal signals to be picked up and immediate responses to be made, so enabling better understanding. It is, however, resource intensive so it is important to ensure that the right medium is used at the right time.

The channel of communication influences both the quality and efficiency of information exchange. Both can be reduced if channels are blocked or if information and decisions are too often received second-hand, via messages or through several levels of bureaucracy. Accessibility and responsiveness are key issues here.

Communication style and skills are also significant. The structure of the communication must be complemented by the right behaviour. For instance, a lack of openness can impede trust and undermine partnership (see Table v).

PCO and health authority relationships: local lessons

There was a wide variation in relationships reflecting differing stages of development in response to earlier policies, local geography and politics, previous experience of joint working, and the impact of other external relationships. The charts that follow depict the results from three of the pilot sites. While these are individual responses, and the numerical scores should be treated with caution and are not directly comparable, they do illustrate the diversity of relationship experiences.

At site 1 the relationship was seen by both health authority and PCO in mostly positive terms with no major areas of weakness or divergence of view. In discussion it emerged that the relationship was principally focused on operational issues, and that the difficult strategic issues which were liable to create tension in the relationships were not at that point being addressed.

At site 2 there was a significant difference in perception of the degree of directness in the

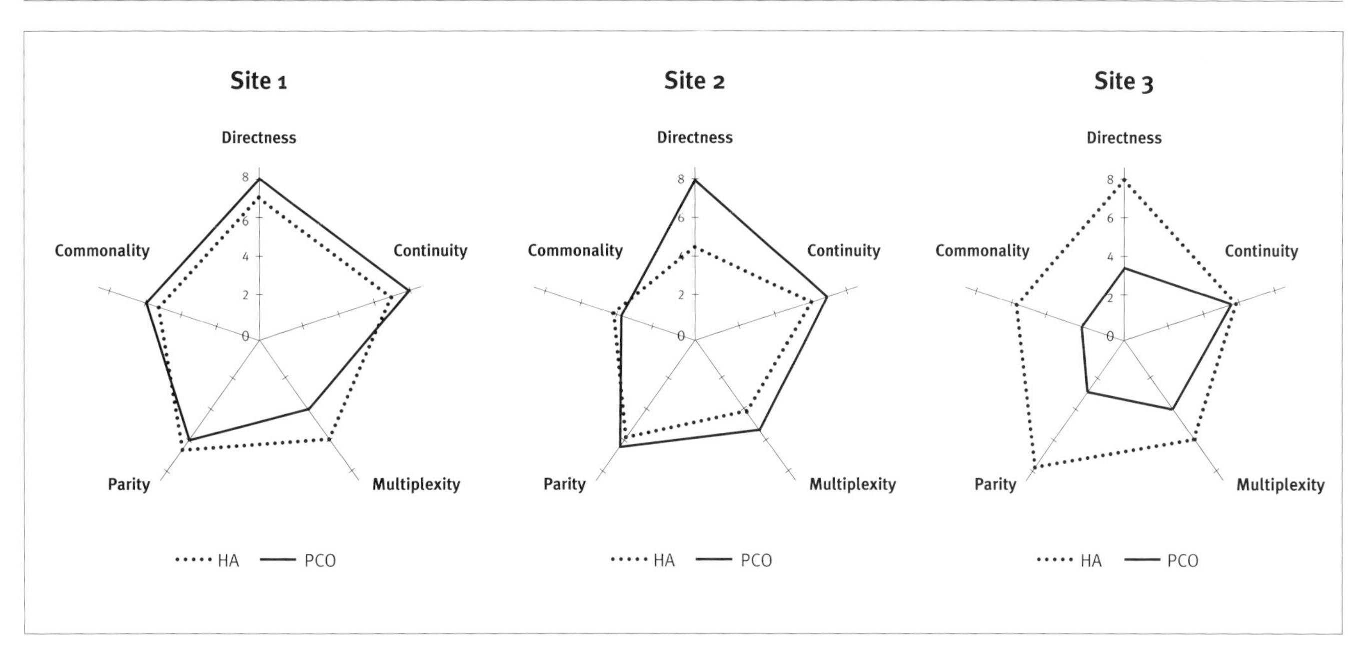

relationship, with a range of concerns being expressed by the health authority. Both the health authority and PCO indicated a lower than average level of commonality in the relationship. Both organisations expressed concerns about different public health priorities, competing organisational interests, different goals for the relationship, and uncertainty as to whether different skills and perspectives were effectively combined.

Site 3 revealed the most divergent perceptions of the relationship, although this in part reflected differing weighting attached to personal and organisational relationships. Although considerable tension was apparent in the relationship, there also appeared to be an underlying robustness in the capacity to address and work through difficult issues.

Despite the diversity of starting points and satisfaction with relationships a number of common issues emerged including:

- superficially good relationships could conceal failure to address important but difficult strategic issues
- rational planning had produced good strategies but without the processes to secure buy-in – adequacy of consultation was perceived very differently
- increased participation by general practices was best gained by promoting the practical advantages, not just the future vision
- health authority automatic assumption of local leadership roles and consequent conduct of the relationship caused resentment. Inclusive leadership was felt to be key to future progress
- conflicting organisational priorities and interests hindered the relationship in all cases
- there was also greater common interest than most participants initially recognised
- professional defensiveness and lack of mutual understanding inhibited progress in a number of cases, although fewer than might have been expected.

Behind these key issues lay significant differences in expectations and perceptions of the relationship.

Commonality

This was in many cases the weakest aspect of the relationship. A lack of commonality was in some cases presumed: for example a belief by health authority staff that GPs were not interested in public health. Such stereotyped views meant that significant areas of common ground had gone unrecognised. While different health ideologies were thought to be a problem in the relationship it was not a major issue between individual participants. There were, however, widespread doubts among participating GPs about how easy it would be to bring colleagues fully on board with them.

There were significant differences in professional cultures, health ideologies and organisational priorities. In many cases these were seen as obstacles to progress with considerable scepticism about whether they could easily be overcome. Those involved in the relationship had built up a degree of shared understanding and objectives, although this was sometimes more around operational than strategic issues. Real shared objectives were only gradually emerging: in many cases this was a consequence of the inadequacies of earlier consultation processes which had failed to secure adequate ownership of the strategies and priorities that emerged as a result. Links between local priorities and health authority-wide priorities were also insufficient.

During the course of the project uncertainty about the role of health authorities in the future (for example as facilitator, power-broker or regulator), caused uncertainty about the extent to which common purpose was attainable. The extent to which health authorities were, or were perceived to be, creating distance in the relationship to strengthen accountability and protect all stakeholder interests; protecting their own organisational interests; or working closely together with the PCOs to ensure the effective implementation of new policies, influenced the nature and extent of the common ground that was expected.

There were some unifying forces. In some cases it was a 'common enemy' such as an overspending acute trust. Where a major part of the public health role was in managing this demand there were wide variations in the extent to which those in primary care recognised this as being to their benefit rather than perceiving the lower involvement in primary care as a lack of interest. A broader focus such as city-wide initiatives could also help bring people together.

In terms of building this aspect of the foundations for a relationship a number of pointers emerged:

- Identify the common ground that does exist to enable early wins (this included integrating other practices)
- Recognise that there are no short cuts to cultural change -- start by working with others' culture rather than threatening it
- The need for inclusive leadership to establish commonality
- Building commonality at a personal level could enable organisational obstacles to be overcome more easily.

Parity

Issues of power in the relationship were complex, with it being common for all parties to feel disempowered. This reflected the different kinds of power operating in the relationship as well as the influence of other relationships. Thus one health authority felt disempowered by the uncertainty surrounding what future central guidance might contain and the uncertainty about their own future role, while their PCOs were frustrated by the health authorities' continuing presumption of the local leadership role and the right to make (in the view of the PCO) unilateral decisions. Divergent expectations and perceptions about leadership and decision-making were one of the major sources of friction in the relationship. Responsibility and accountability were out of alignment, with nationally imposed tight timetables and, in some cases, local divisions constraining effective consultation. Differing expectations of future change led to differing views of how roles should develop. Issues of parity between health professionals were not a focus of this project but were an influential background factor.

Multiplexity

There was considerable uncertainty as to the extent to which there was good mutual understanding of each other's organisations, their individual skills and interests, and the particular pressures and constraints each had to work with. Myths and stereotypes affecting attitudes and belief in the potential of the relationships meant that significant areas of common ground were, in some cases, unrecognised. Opportunities for progress had been missed as a result. The limited breadth in the relationship was partly a consequence of the communication pattern. Where much of the contact had been over operational issues or formal consultation processes there had been few opportunities to build a broader understanding of each other's work or organisations. Having public health professionals with a background in general practice was seen to be helpful in enabling this understanding to be built up.

Continuity

Individuals had in most cases known each other several years and had developed good personal working relationships. A period of constant organisational change meant that these had not translated into good organisational relationships. For one participating health authority the average lifetime of a job was 18 months, with there being, on average, two postholders during this period. This was not unusual. Investment in relationships was perceived to be time well spent, though not always easy to achieve.

There was universal agreement that not

enough attention was devoted to long-term issues affecting the relationship between health authorities and new primary care organisations. This was partly a consequence of the immediate pressures of policy implementation deadlines.

Directness

Communication channels appeared to be reasonably effective. In some cases there were concerns about the prevalence of hidden agendas and uncertainty about what counterparts really thought. Some concern was felt about 'real' listening and whether meetings were at the right time. In most cases the participants represented the most developed aspects of local health authority/PCO relationships. It is likely that these were not necessarily typical of the majority of local relationships, where levels of contact, trust and directness may well be lower.

The emerging development agenda

Overall, this stage of the project served to highlight the lack of a partnership approach to the process of health strategy development and particularly the rather variable, although changing, quality of relationship between primary care organisations and health authorities around issues of health improvement. Clearly the extent of primary care involvement and quality of relationships varied between the sites. Each site had very different experiences, histories and other local contextual factors that provide the starting point for taking forward the new public health agenda. The discussion of the findings in local workshops supported participants' thinking about the future role of PCGs in improving health as well as the delivery of health care with important implications particularly for organisational development. This was at a time of considerable uncertainty and change.

Important early lessons and questions were considered. Both exercises showed the marked lack of commonality between the primary care organisations and health authorities – the lack of a sense of common interest around which a shared common purpose for improving health of local communities could be pursued, and that simultaneously advanced 'district' priorities. Participants had very different perceptions of what health, health improvement and health strategies meant. This was often exemplified by the cited different professional perspectives of primary care and public health, in which primary care concerns itself with the health and health care of individuals, whilst public health takes a population approach. This dichotomy, however false, has been real in its consequences, as it has often been translated into public health and primary care personnel holding quite pronounced stereotypes of each other.

Other inter-related issues and questions raised included:

- To what extent is primary care changing? To what extent is there actually a shift from the primary *medical* care (disease-based) to the primary *health* care model based on the principles of inter-agency working, community involvement and equity; the model that is required if the wider public health agenda is to be addressed?
- To what extent are the new emerging primary care organisations developing a community approach? How does this relate to the 'population approach' advocated by public health? Do 'populations' need to be more locally defined to engage primary care practitioners? What are the implications for evidence-based public health?
- How do we develop public health capacity and organisational capacity in primary care? What kind of competencies are needed? Should these be 'in-house', for example community nursing, or accessible from elsewhere? What are the implications for health authority public health departments?
- How can primary care develop effective relationships beyond the NHS? Current links with local authorities were mostly confined to social services, but these need to be extended to other departments, including housing, environmental health, transport, leisure services, urban renewal, etc.

These issues were further explored in the subsequent stages of the project. They are clearly part of the future strategic agenda for the development of the primary health care model that is demanded by the new policy framework. Chapter 3 reports on the subsequent stages of the project which focused more on the participants' experiences of taking the agenda forward and also on how primary care could change over the longer term to deliver both improvements in health as well as health care. In particular, it reports the findings of a scenario planning exercise, which recognised that PCGs and health authorities are at very different starting points and consequently reveals that different development pathways are likely, and required, in order to make progress. Central policy development, of course, will need to be sensitive to these local needs.

References

Department of Health (1998a). *Our healthier nation: a contract for health.* London: Stationery Office.

Department of Health (1998b). *The health of the nation – a policy assessed.* London: Stationery Office.

Gibb, A (1995). What is a small business?, *Networker Supplement*, No. 3, Durham University Business School.

Wheeler, D and Sillanpaa, M (1997). *The stakeholder corporation.* London: Pitman.

Southampton and South West Hampshire case study

Summary

A district of 550,000 population with six primary care groups which were expected to be at level 2 by April 1999. Three PCGs (Central, East and West) cover the city, a new unitary authority. There is a history of active involvement by GPs in general practice fundholding (GPFH), a Total Purchasing Pilot, a GP Commissioning Pilot, multifunds and consortia. There is one large teaching hospital, a local community trust and four other significant providers. Primary care is regarded as being underinvested: the health authority is seeking to contain spending on acute services within its current level of total expenditure as a maximum and seek to reduce this over time.

Progress

Within the city of Southampton one of the PCGs is well on track with the other two still encountering some difficulties. Public health strategy development builds on the previous experience of every practice doing health plans – a health authority-wide initiative. This is becoming more locality focused and moving away from a more disease-based rational planning approach. Tensions are mainly over priority-setting and money.

The Southampton Central PCG is able to build on the foundation of the Commissioning Pilot (set up in 1996) and the developing co-operation associated with its establishment and initial work. Concern about poor services was the first significant recognition of common interests and, in the absence of effective health authority action, prompted work together to take forward local commissioning. The initial core tried to draw other practices in through the demonstrated benefits of joint working such as the ability to buy in physiotherapy services.

The locality was split into neighbourhood teams with populations of about 10,000 to create neighbourhood nursing teams which coincide with local authority community action forums. This helped overcome the problem of different primary care team structures and helped develop relationships through continually meeting the same people as well as allowing mutual influence of agendas.

Key public health priorities have been decided by primary care teams with prioritisation of issues continuing within sub-groups of the PCG. There are four sub-groups exploring prescribing, mental health, service development with trusts, and ethnic minorities.

Partnership with NHS trusts has been important, recognising that 'their problems are our problem'. This has involved meeting with clinical directorates to develop intermediate care schemes.

Problems

From the health authority perspective PCG development problems have arisen from a leadership vacuum created by the authority not stepping in early enough to facilitate progress at an inter-practice level. Some practices are perceived to be isolationist, not sharing ideas and experience.

From the PCG perspective, while the health authority is regarded as good at planning and committed to consultation, the processes have in the past been weak with concerns about the language, focus and whether contributions are listened to. 'Retired hurt' was the outcome of some initial encounters. However, the improvements in this are recognised with commitment to greater openness and partnerships. Health Improvement Programmes are seen as an opportunity for further improvement of the strategy process.

While PCG board members are committed there are some concerns about the commitment of other partners and the potential to sustain enthusiasm if not adequately resourced.

Messages

- Primary and secondary care must work together on priorities
- The importance of the process of development of strategy in enabling the PCGs to mature and take on harder issues needs to be recongised.

(November 1998)

3. Delivery: towards the public health agenda. How primary care organisations can improve health as well as deliver effective health care

Re-processing the NHS

'If our litmus test is how successfully we restructure then we have failed' (HA head of organisational development)

When this project was first conceived, in June 1997, the general practice could be viewed as still sovereign and the term 'primary care group' had yet to be coined. Although primary care organisations were then emerging, in some areas, as new collective arrangements, these were essentially driven by the economic and clinical imperatives of more efficient secondary care contracting and emergency cover, rather than by the principles and the broader objectives of 'primary health care' as set out in Chapter 1. The project invited participation from the diverse range of primary care-led models of commissioning that had evolved. References to a thousand flowers beginning to bloom (Mays and Dixon, 1996), in respect of individual initiatives in primary care, bore witness to the organisational diversity and fragmentation which the central policy values of consumer choice, provider autonomy and professional opportunity had successfully helped to promote (NHS Executive, 1996a).

In 1996/97 within the space of nine months there had been, after all, a succession of no fewer than four major governmental policy initiatives designed to both extend and reinforce the role of the general practitioner as the managing agent for secondary services and the principal focus for medical care (NHS Executive, 1996a, b and c which led to the 1997 NHS (Primary Care) Act). Primary care had never before received such central attention, but this unprecedented period in the political spotlight did little to promote either the concept of primary health care based on the WHO principles or the rather different organisational capacity this would require. On the other hand, it did represent an intense period of structural re-engineering that would be hard to undo. The espousal of primary health care and its basic principles would require a new approach. Many of those who had worked in both the professions of primary care and public health would be required, for the first time, to take the long-term strategic view encompassing a range of community interests often well beyond the conventional boundaries of the NHS.

'Previously any initiatives in terms of new primary care organisations were only really seen as GP business projects – they had little to do with the overall purpose of the NHS' (TPP Manager)

The subsequent 18 months of this project have witnessed the beginnings of this approach. Through redefining primary care to incorporate public health, and vice versa, organisational developments are under way which signify the re-processing of the NHS. It is not simply general practice that is being transformed. As the basic unit of primary care shifts so too does the entire organisational framework of the health care system. This means more than merely the transfer of operational functions on the one hand, or policy presentations about 'New partnerships' on the other (Dobson, 1997).

The relational mapping exercises with health authority participants in the project described in Chapter 2, revealed fundamental changes in the relationship profiles of those authorities: upwards and outwards in the future, no longer downwards and inward-looking. As health authorities take on strategic responsibilities for the central NHS, their relationships are developing with co-regulators such as the Housing Corporation and the NHS Ombudsman. The emerging health authority has neither the capacity nor the commitment to relate to individual practices – except in special circumstances – and all the health authority representatives were united in their view that by the year 2000 the primary care group has to be *the* unit of primary care organisation. It is only at this level, with this critical mass, that the design of the health system can be adjusted to achieve the radical realignment of inter-agency relationships that promoting public health requires.

> *'Health authorities are the "New Regions"'*
> (HA director of primary care)

Conversely for general practices the world is also changing fundamentally. Within primary care groups they are aware of being instrumental in delivering a new mixed economy of frontline care. The participants in the project were able to list the following different types of organisational status as important means of achieving higher levels of future resource investment in primary care:

(i) HA sub-committee (public)
(ii) prospective NHS primary care trust (with access to Private Finance Initiative)
(iii) legal partnership (independent)
(iv) limited company (private)
(v) joint venture (commercial)
(vi) charitable trust (voluntary)
(vii) local patients' association (community).

Each of the above is already part of a primary care group. Each of the above requires a different and separate framework of accountability. The principles of participation and intersectoral alliances which underpin the concept of primary health care, and its overarching emphasis on equity for health (Macdonald, 1992), rather than simply of resources, services or outputs, provide a pragmatic as well as a philosophical means of progressing contemporary organisational developments in this context.

> *'We are all primary health care workers now'*
> (GP chair of a PCG)

In action research mode (Edwards and Talbot, 1994) the project responded to the publication of the *New NHS* White Paper and the *Healthier nation* consultative document. The brief recognised in January 1998 that it is the primary care groups which will be responsible for promoting the health of their local populations, and the development of primary care (including the health promotion and disease prevention services); as well as commissioning the large majority of health services. Primary care groups would 'grow out' of earlier models. The revised project objectives recognised that it is PCGs which, with health authorities and others, 'will set targets for improvements in health and health care, and be held accountable.'

> *'After Christmas (1998) for most health authorities the penny suddenly dropped: PCGs are the future. But too many GPs are not there yet.'*
> (exchange between two consultants in public health, the first attached to a PCG, the second based in a health authority)

Fight/flight

> *'The day will be wonderful when you disappear.'*
>
> *'They are only interested in lining their pockets.'* (summary by an HA head of health promotion of a stereotypical GP view of a health authority, and vice versa)

The strength of historic attitudinal difference as much as the structural separation of general practice has meant that the move towards primary health care as an organisational development is fraught with tension, and casualties as well, as the project itself vividly demonstrated.

One of the initial applicants to join the project as a new primary care organisation was a local cluster of general practices, each engaged in negotiating a local service contract under the terms of the 1997 NHS (Primary Care) Act. The enterprise was dismantled as a result of inter-practice difficulties even before the initial questionnaire survey could be completed in March 1998. At the same time similar but more personalised individual 'lead GP' rivalries were leading to the withdrawal from the project of a Total Purchasing Pilot two hundred miles away. Fortunately, and interestingly, however, its local counterpart – another TPP a few miles away on the outskirts of London – did survive and successfully convert into a primary care group with a clear township identity and focus on addressing specific local areas of urban deprivation. This was an early practical example of the unifying effect that moving towards an organisational focus on primary health care can bring about.

> *'Retired hurt'* (words used by both an HA chief executive and GP chair of a PCG to summarise initial GP/HA negotiations)

The damage was at least as severe for the participating health authorities. Throughout the project there were numerous examples of good practice in primary health care derived from the creative energies of individual entrepreneurs. The primary care team-led asthma management training programmes for schoolteachers in Oldham is one example; the HEALS (Healthy Living in Sneinton and St Ann's) project linking ten general practices to local schools in Nottinghamshire to develop a common curriculum for health promotion is another. Both of these were nurtured and supported by sympathetic health authority primary care 'leads'. In three of the health districts originally signed up to the project in the autumn of 1997 these individuals had left without replacement within a year. In one case the primary care directorate was disbanded in the same month as the first primary care group's central guidance was issued (March 1998). As the project drew to its conclusion a number of health authority personnel with long-standing Family Health Services experience were placed in 'clearing houses' with the prospect of possible early redundancy facing them.

> *'Changing to primary health care depends on individuals not organisations; like general practice in the end it has to be an act of faith.'* (local GP)

Organisational theorists have frequently commented upon the profound ambivalence that accompanies formative organisational developments. The need to recognise and address the inevitable forces of resistance and inertia in delivering a new agenda is brought sharply into focus, in terms of primary care groups and the move towards primary health care, by examples such as those described above. The importance of not simply identifying and celebrating early successes, but also, more prosaically but fundamentally, achieving practical alliances around such bottom-line lowest common denominators as staying within budget, maintaining public confidence and keeping control of waiting lists, was frequently apparent.

A common enemy could fit the bill. In two of the project's major cities the health authority and emerging primary care groups forged their first alliance as a reaction to what they both perceived as consultant-controlled, overweening and over-spending university hospitals. In both cases local health strategies simply did not exist as a basis for coming together. Before 1998, partly as a result of secondary care influences, those strategies that did exist were service-based, disease-specific health-care programmes.

> *'In the big cities it is the city which is the natural community – for future primary care purposes'* (HA director of community health services commissioning)

In two of the project's participating larger towns it was a shared cause rather than a common enemy that supplied the starting point. The preservation of a community hospital in the first case and a casualty unit in the second paved the way for local exploration of what the future strategic focus should be. The perspective for primary care automatically moved beyond the practice and paradoxically, as in the districts where there had either been no new health strategies written since 1995, or only a total of three client group priorities ever produced, a blank sheet of paper was actually a positive asset in starting over again.

The NHS and those it is used to working with in England have not yet reached the stage of tackling the health status of the population and community development. Operational pressures, risks, and, sometimes opportunities, are the currency of relationships, from which primary health care has to emerge. In one district this meant starting with the daily hotspots in the surgery – back pain and hypertension – as the basis for attaching consultants in public health to local primary care groups. In others, where fundholding was widespread and effective, the General Practice Fundholding contracts for hospital and community health services helped provide a secure basis from which to move into a genuine exchange over the Health Improvement Programme and Service and Financial Frameworks. The fragility of primary health care, linked inextricably to the vulnerability of key individuals and their roles during a decade of continuous organisational change in the NHS, indicates the importance of building carefully, and incrementally for primary health care. As one director of public health put it: 'The patchwork approach is everything.'

> *'How can we provide organisational development for primary care groups when we are still on five sites?' (after successive DHA/FHSA mergers)* (HA director of primary care and ex-FHSA chief executive)

A winning constituency – for improving public health as well as delivering effective health care

> *'There have been a lot of turf wars'* (HA chief executive)

In direct contract with both the national government and individual citizen British general practice has become accustomed to occupying, and usually enjoying, a unique political position (Boaden, 1997). To modify this so that, for example, the concept of partnership in primary care no longer converts into the uni-professional ownership of the main organisational unit requires a fine balance of strength and sensitivity. In organisational terms primary health care is at the opposite end of the spectrum to primary medical care: intersectoral, inter-agency and, above all, interprofessional (Starfield, 1992).

> *'We haven't had the debate yet. We are just at the stage of accepting that there may be changes in our roles; but we don't yet know what they will be'*
> (GP chair of a PCG)

The project saw both these extremes as practical realities. In two districts espoused central policies for primary health care were being expressed through quarterly local health forums for all primary care professionals, with widespread support from, for example, local pharmacists and optometrists. In another, more than 300 people had taken part in city-wide 'Vision for Primary and Community Care' local workshops, while on the South Coast 120 organisational representatives had attended a health authority-sponsored event designed to help primary care groups identify the new opportunities for local health partnerships arising by the year 2001. These creative endeavours, however, were exceptional. At the other end of the spectrum was the year-long deferment of work on the Health Improvement Programme in one district where the primary care groups were set up to directly inherit and implement the health authority's purchasing plan. Here the initial PCG meetings were for health authority personnel and GPs only, with fundholding GPs in the overwhelming majority. In another district the exclusion of other primary care professionals led to what a senior nurse described as 'the complete alienation of the PAMs'.

> *'I don't know what you are talking to the director of public health for. He's got nothing to do with primary care groups!'*
> (HA chief executive)

These quasi-tribal interprofessional difficulties were not without their means of resolution. In most of the project's participating districts there was confidence that, over time, the new political paradigm for primary care could be created and sustained to replace that which has maintained the general medical practitioner and primary medical care since the inception of the NHS.

This optimism had two common sources: first, effective role differentiation in primary care groups; and secondly the recognition that the practice and the locality should be separated for the different purposes of primary care service delivery and its future planning for community health improvement. The latter even resulted in a number of GP participants in the project arguing for more 'meeting time and space' to develop local health strategies, an unheard-of request in pre-May 1997 times.

'The agenda is large enough for everybody to have a role and to make a contribution.'
(GP chair of PCG)

Primary care groups emerging successfully with a strategic perspective for primary health-care orientation appear to have the capacity to articulate and address both the vision and the uncertainty. The first is releasing a considerable untapped personal and professional potential, legitimising, for example, the sickness prevention programmes which have previously passed unpaid for and unheralded by some individual general practices. The challenge of articulating a local vision for primary health care was evidently being taken up by some of the new PCG chairs and leaders via, for example: the development of a PCG-wide community stroke programme; a public health database for the over-75s; and a rota of factory screening visits. As important, however, as this emerging generation of primary care visionaries, is the older existing generation of wise and respected senior citizens in primary care.

The senior GP was especially important here, where he or she could be universally understood as an impartial, authoritative, and, above all, inclusive figure. Such symbols of maturity are, for example, currently critical to the successful organisational developments in the project's participating districts of Leeds, North and Mid-Hampshire and West Hertfordshire; as well as districts such as Wolverhampton, Camden and Islington, and West Surrey where training material from the project has been requested and applied.

The origins of these figures have varied. There is no consistent pattern. Their emergence appears to be more a case of situational requirements than any motivation for personal leadership. In different primary care groups, the individuals were drawn from the local medical committee, the postgraduate education advisers and the Primary Care Alliance – to name but three sources. In each case the function, however, was broadly the same: to broker the birth of a broad church for primary health care.

'Our job is to support primary care not just GPs'
(local medical committee secretary)

The distinction between the practice and the locality is proving a tougher cultural challenge. This was true for district participants in the project where primary care has always been associated with high performance, as well as for those at the other end of the ladder. Dorset, for example, recognised that its successes had been essentially practice based and that as a result it would need to move towards primary care groups through a level 1 point of entry and much smaller units of population coverage than the 100,000 norm recommended by the NHS Executive. In August 1998, accordingly, the ten Dorset PCG applications had an average population size of less than 70,000. Here the general practice plan had become the established individual unit for business planning, local health-care delivery and financial monitoring. Strategic alliances for health were peripheral to its remit. Elsewhere, of course, other districts were far from being so far advanced. In one area an attempt to introduce practice-based health needs assessment programmes across nineteen general practices had failed in all but three; while in two others professional opposition and probity issues prevented the attempt from even being undertaken.

'In this day and age is a single-handed practice in any way, shape or form appropriate?' (senior manager of NHS community trust)

The need for a distinction, therefore, between responsibilities for service delivery and planning within primary care groups, at least at this stage of their organisational development, was especially important. Amongst the project's participating districts this was most positively recognised by West Hertfordshire, where for several years the director of public health – himself a former general medical practitioner – had fed back comparative health status information and intelligence to practices on the basis of their local wards, parishes and coterminous district council/social services areas. In Leeds too sixteen local areas had been identified for data capture and commissioning, although attempts to form primary care groups coterminous with clusters of these encountered severe difficulties. In some instances the legacy of past GP partnership splits proved too strong.

Nevertheless, on the basis of a clear differentiation of roles for the practice and the locality, the evidence of the project suggested that primary care groups can achieve a viable organisational identity, and one that is accepted as legitimate by GPs and others in terms of primary health-care leadership and advocacy of community health improvements with relative alacrity. In West Hertfordshire, for example, the PCG support was seen as an important ingredient in the successful bid for European Union funding to support anti-deprivation initiatives in Borehamwood and South Oxhey. In Dorset, Southampton and West Surrey the same applied to applications for personal medical services pilot status. Above all it is at the level of the locality that most emerging primary care groups recognised that the new partnerships should be formed; whether they be with the local recreation centre for exercise prescription schemes, or with the pharmaceutical company for epilepsy care or an overall pharmacy benefits management package.

'Local contracts for primary health care – that is crossing the Rubicon!'
(HA director of public health)

Organisational developments

'There is no à la carte menu'
(HA director of public health)

Central NHS Executive policy guidance defined four levels of primary care groups (see table). Conceptually participants in the project found this helpful. It assisted in giving definition to local reflection and debate, and in locating broadly where local participants were. In terms of a framework of actual organisational developments, however, it proved to be of less positive value. These developments did not follow the intellectually neat and satisfying sequence of the central documents. The dynamics of the organisational development relationships pointed to a much less linear progression, with important implications for primary care groups as future pivotal agents of health strategy. Indeed, in using collectively their present material to predict the pattern of future organisational developments the project highlighted significant concerns about the direction of travel for some primary care groups, with the suggestion that at least a further, fifth level is required if primary care organisations are truly to deliver effective health care as well as contribute to better public health.

Participants in the project were well aware of the risks as well as the opportunities arising from the translation of general practice into new primary care organisations. To an extent they felt themselves to be on trial. They are aware

Primary care groups

Level \ Structure	Role and responsibilities
One	As a minimum to act in support of the health authority in commissioning care for the district population, acting in an advisory capacity
Two	To take devolved responsibility for managing the budget for health care in their PCG area, acting as a committee of the health authority.
Three	As a primary care trust to become established as a free-standing body accountable to the health authority for the commissioning of health care.
Four	As for Level Three but with additional responsibility for the provision of community health services to the population in the PCG area.

Source: Department of Health (1998)

that, if popular expectations of a long-term Labour government are fulfilled, there may well be further major policy initiatives ahead. Already they are conscious of different models of primary care being taken forward in the different parts of the United Kingdom.* Accordingly, there was a readiness to test best- and worst-case scenarios, and to pool existing examples of actual organisational developments on the ground in primary care. Together these constituted productive raw material for moving well beyond the centrally defined hierarchy of four primary care group levels.

The result of this collective intelligence gathering exercise and the consequent organisational analysis is shown in the table on page 36. Four distinct organisational types could be distinguished, using an analysis of differences in organisational purpose and objectives, management arrangements, health strategies and public health functions, information sources and internal and external relationships. On the basis of this analysis, designed to understand if a genuine organisational capacity to undertake primary health care is being developed in practice, four organisational models with separate principal accountabilities could be delineated. Unlike, however, the four conceptual levels these four organisational developments are clearly not a natural progression. Indeed to move from one category into the next, in each case, would be a painful process.

The first organisational type, the 'Defence association' appears reactionary, but at its heart is its profound concern for the individual as a complete human being. In terms of public health it would be a serious mistake to write it off. The same applies to the 'Friendly society' for all its costs and inefficiencies. It is an important vehicle for creating the momentum for local health strategies, just as the type C 'Executive agency' offers a means of converting good intentions into effective implementation. But this type is essentially narrow in its power base and only at the fourth stage, the 'Franchised company', are there the first signs of a primary care organisation beginning to adjust its relationships and engage with local community interests on issues of public health improvement.

Participants in the project, although drawn from some of the 'leading edge' parts of the NHS, had no difficulty at all in recognising as commonplace type A: the primary care group as defence association. Indeed this was generally felt to be in many parts of the country the most natural form of organisational development, representing a true alignment with past professional traditions in primary care and the conventional role of general practices in both the social and political systems at local and national levels. Nobody underestimated the continuing strength of this resistance movement.

> *'The "die-hard" attitudes of doctors and social workers – they can simply reinforce each other.'* (GP chair of a PCG)

Type B, the 'Friendly society' model was the most numerous in the project's participating districts, as they approached 1 April 1999 and the formal launch date for primary care groups in England. It equates fairly closely with the level 2 health authority sub-committee described in the central policy guidance (NHSE, 1998). It feels good. Most people like the idea; it is a model that encourages widespread involvement. The concerns, on the other hand, are about operational efficiency and effectiveness. By April 1999 these were becoming increasingly urgent. Type B's inclusive approach is costly in terms of time and money. Broad churches of primary care professionals do not come cheap; and certainly exceed the limits of health authorities' centrally allocated management allowances for primary care groups. In addition, for the professionals themselves there was a growing frustration at the focus on 'talk' not 'action'; and in this model ultimately there seems little that can be done to redress the balance. The health authority has the power; it remains in control. If the new primary care organisation is to take responsibility as a major unit of NHS performance in its own right for delivering better public health as well as more effective health care, it has to move on.

> *'Level 2 is just a glorified health authority.'* (university academic researching primary care organisations)

But moving on, is not moving to type C. They are different creatures and unrelated. Type C, of all the organisational models, has in some ways

*See, for example, the Local Health Group and Local Health Care Co-operative models set out in, respectively: NHS Wales, *Putting patients first* (Welsh Office, Cardiff, 1998); and Scottish Office/ Department of Health, *Designed to care: renewing the National Health Service in Scotland* (Stationery Office, London, 1997).

Type	A Defence association	B Friendly society	C Executive agency	D Franchised company
Status	Professional network	HA sub-committee	Brokers' firm	Mixed status public utility
Account-ability (to)	DoH/GPC	HA/LMC	Trusts	National/regional regulators
Purpose	To advocate and represent individual general practice interests for growth and survival	To encourage an inclusive approach to local health issues, based on existing practice arrangements	To constrain secondary care and re-direct resources to practices	To control majority health-care resources of local population and seek a health dividend
Objectives	(i) To sustain GMS income (ii) To preserve practice configuration (iii) To defend professional autonomy (iv) To respond effectively to local consultations on health issues	(i) To support HA as principal purchaser of health care ii) To promote primary care teams with GP leadership (iii) To explore opportunities for inter-practice collaboration (iv) To maintain district as NHS performance unit	(i) To release critical mass of GPs for general medical practice (ii) To set direction for community health services (iii) To explore scope for improved skills substitution and inter-professional working (iv) To resolve secondary/ primary care conflicts via inter-clinician deals and trade-offs	(i) To operate as a corporate organisation in terms of investment and savings (ii) To address population and individual health issues in balance (iii) To gain community acceptance and active endorsement (iv) To radically revise both GMS and HCHS working practices
Management (by)	Liaison GPs and HA middle manager 'links'	Commissioning (non-GPFH) GPs plus HA purchasing/ corporate services managers	Former GPFH leads and managers – from practices and trusts	Senior community trust or HA executives, plus 'new' primary care professional leads on primary health care
Health strategy	Operational responses to nationally determined policies and contracts	Derived from DPH annual report and profiles of patient demand, augmented by effective individual representations	Intermediate care-based – avoidable A & Es, continuing care, acute episodes, etc. Influenced by SSD community care plans	Based on Patient Enrolment Principle – registered population signed up to organisation's health business priorities – as described in trust prospectus
Public health (function)	Very limited personnel resources, focused on core roles of communicable diseases, HNA, etc.	Operationally aligned with HA commissioning directorate. Closely involved in secondary care and clinical effectiveness issues	Promoting public health issues and alliances at strategic levels with unitary authorities or commerce, etc.; via shared SLAs	Split between overall performance monitoring and outposted advisory roles; leading multi-professional public health networks including health visitors
Information	Extrapolated from national data sources (e.g. ONS, DoH, MDS)	Locality analyses at parish/ ward levels by HA based on NHS morbidity and hospital referral categories	Combined with LAs, and based on district council/ municipal boundaries; including CHS profiles	Built up from practice level health needs assessments, and combined with information sources of three other PCO types, plus literature/research findings
Internal relations (key)	Individual GP-based, with small and single-handed practices prominent. Strong support from practice administrative staff	Inter-practice forums and committees (e.g. audit, PGE), plus HA functions for contracting/commissioning	Paramedical staff; full range of community nursing, 'lead' GPs	
External relations (key)	GPC; individual patients, traditional NHS managers, RCGP (national)	HA members and chief executive, prescribing adviser, primary care alliance, RCGP (regions), hospital consultants	Community trust service clinicians and managers, social services, budget managers, health economists, accountants; voluntary organisations; Association for Primary Care	New primary care trusts national group; NICE/CHIMP, NHSE, regional offices/ assemblies, media and politicians; commercial sector, major providers
Organisational prospects	Limited life expectancy	Transitional	Temporary	Fragile basis for future organisational development

the least to do with public health. At best its interest is tactical rather than strategic. The popular image here is that of the fast-lane city broker. It is too simple to say that the type C organisation, examples of which were identified everywhere but more especially in the shire county towns, is GP fundholding writ large. It is rather a product of a number of local forces in which the defensiveness of hospital clinicians and the conservativeness of the majority of general practitioners, are at least as significant as the presence of a small number of primary care professionals and managers who have developed well-honed negotiating and contracting skills.

The type C organisation can develop relatively smoothly out of type A, and the classic examples of this in the project were North Hampshire and Nottingham where local senior managers from the local NHS community trust with PCG project management responsibilities had been instrumental in the delivery. This delivery can demonstrate tangible service products – selective reductions in waiting lists, intermediate care programmes; shared facilities and training programmes across general medical and community health services staff are obvious examples – but its change agenda is internally defined. Population health issues are, on the whole, something different and in another place. Accordingly, as an organisational development it is immature, its fragility illustrated by PCG members' anxiety about their mandate and future electability. The implications for level 3 NHS trust applications by primary care groups can be considered in relation to this perspective. At this stage this level appears to signify either a 'half-way house' or a 'no-man's land', indicating that the local health care system as a whole, including the health authority itself, has not yet acquired the relational maturity to move forward together in a strategic way on issues of population health. The trust, tolerance and confidence in each other is not yet there.

> *'Strategy is something you do; and we don't implement!'* (GP chair of a PCG to health authority executive board members)

Type D is getting closer to an organisational model for primary health care, but its difficulties unlike those of type C, are predominantly with its internal rather than its strategic external relationships, and their neglect. Type D and type B are allies. Indeed the former may represent an escape route for the latter. At this stage, however, few organisational developments with a comprehensive approach to assuming a franchised responsibility for the local population's health and health care actually exist in either structural shape or process design. In the majority of the project's participating districts, however, this was the aspiration; and within a relatively short timescale – 2001 was the most frequently cited target date. The readiness of the health authority to devolve roles and responsibilities; a critical mass of interprofessional primary care teams; and systematic local health information and planning arrangements are key ingredients in this stage of organisational development. The technical infrastructure, however, is tending to outstrip the personal and social dimensions. General practice will not easily pass away as the leading unit of primary care in England. In all sorts of ways there is too much capital invested in it for the move to organisations characterised by the features of primary health care to be either smooth or speedy.

> *'There is always the risk of marital breakdown.'* (social services member of a PCG)

As a result with a fourfold increase simply in the scale of their external relationships the type D organisational development neglects its internal, inter- and intra-practice relationships at its peril. Unhappily, however, because of the level of new demands and their very novelty they may also fall foul of this temptation all too easily. Such was the lesson of the cross-district participants in three workshop simulations held at the City University in 1998, when the project data were used to help shape the exercise. In each case the level 4 primary care group virtually imploded. By failing to consider its own health it disqualified itself from addressing others.

> *'Primary care groups – like mixing oil and water'* (health authority director of public health)

Organisational delivery

Modern organisations are different from those which have conventionally used the production models of manufacturing industry or bureaucratic public authorities as their reference points. They are less formally defined and discrete, less institutional, and where successful, more responsive to their environments. As traditional community support mechanisms at the level of the neighbourhood, church and nuclear family tend to diminish, modern organisations may increasingly have to meet the social and personal needs of their members (Drucker, 1995; Etzioni, 1994). Primary care groups and, prospectively, primary care trusts are emerging as potential leading examples of such modern prototypes and where they genuinely commit themselves to a health as well as a health-care agenda then their potential human resource, given the changing nature of organisations, is considerably enlarged. The prospects for health could be dynamic with the primary care organisation itself becoming a source of health for its members.

For these prospects to be realised primary care organisations clearly need to achieve not just the right sort of vision but also be able to draw on the necessary combinations of resources and competencies, and to integrate them effectively regardless of where they come from. The challenge of 'organisation', literally, is that much harder, notwithstanding the positive cultural messages that the renewed central policy emphasis on overall 'integration' provides (Department of Health, 1998).

With this in mind, the project participants spent a day in November 1998 applying an analytical framework designed to identify the seven dimensions of a well-integrated organisation to the four primary care group types described and discussed earlier in this chapter. The framework was drawn from the work of Peters and Waterman, and uses some of the learning gained from studying the management of international corporations (Peters and Waterman, 1980). The framework is set out in the figure.

Analytical framework of a well-integrated organisation

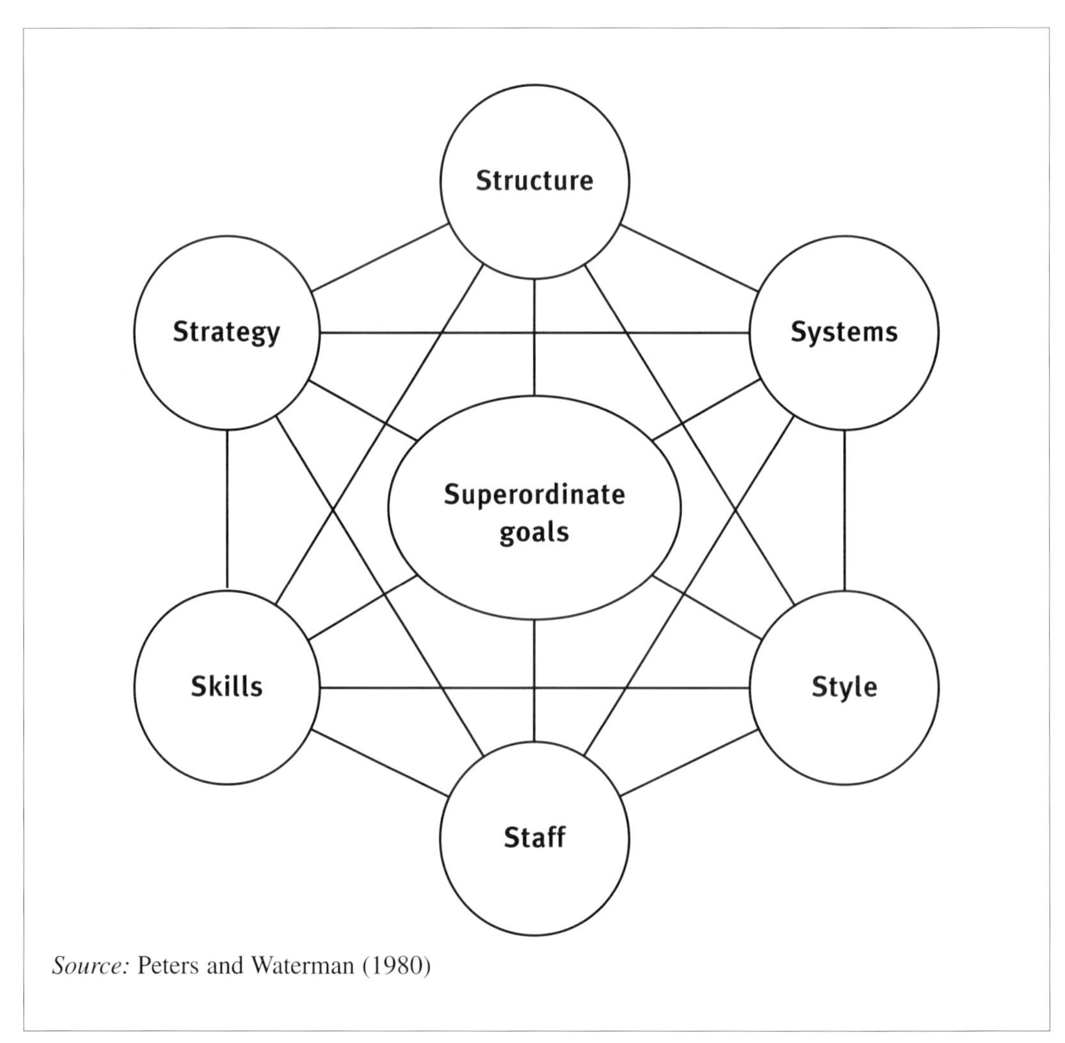

Source: Peters and Waterman (1980)

The seven organisational dimensions are: strategy, structure, systems, style, staff, skills and superordinate goals (or culture). The thinking behind this seven 'S' framework is that an organisation earns this title only when each and all of these dimensions are in support of each other. It is a model well suited for use by modern organisations that constitute not simply staff but a much wider variety of stakeholders and participants (Iles, 1997).

In this analysis strategy is understood as the actions planned by the organisation in response to, or anticipation of, changes in its external environment, which includes the patient, public and organisational/sectoral interfaces. Structure serves as the mechanism for differentiating and integrating roles and responsibilities, and together with an organisation's systems is the vehicle for workload management. Accordingly the term 'systems' covers such functions as budgets, training and audit and includes both formal and informal procedures. Staff and skills are the organisational resource base covering both the technical and behavioural attributes required of the organisation; and style refers to its values and priorities and the way they are expressed, particularly by high status participants in the organisation.

When these six elements are in harmony the seventh 'S' applies: 'superordinate goals'. The organisation has a discernible common culture or cause. Public health and its promotion would fit the bill nicely. Unfortunately for each of the four primary care organisational types identified in the project this was not quite the outcome. The conclusion was that primary care groups are a transitional stage. The primary health-care organisation capable of effectively pursuing community health improvements is yet to come.

Organisational outcomes

Using a checklist of questions set out under the headings of the seven 'S' framework the November 1998 workshop members developed four organisational products. These have subsequently attracted considerable local interest, particularly from organisers of similar local training exercises with primary care group participants elsewhere. As a result the outcomes have been further reviewed and revised. A summary of the outcomes follows.

Type A: The defence association

Two different forms were identified:

- A1 – characterised by suburban fundholders 'defending' strong practices
- A2 – characterised by inner-city single-handers with potentially less developed practices.

A. Strategy

In this model public health strategy is external to primary care groups and driven by the health authority. The health authority's approach to public health is therefore critical. Priorities are likely to be more meaningful at practice than primary care board level and reflect nationally set priorities, financial incentives, and main areas of dissatisfaction with current service provision.

However, from the health authority perspective:

- strategy may officially be focused around developing a primary care group
- but it may not actually want a full primary care group to develop so that the health authority keeps control
- in some cases there may be potential to bypass primary care groups and focus on such alternative change agents as Health Action Zones. Overall a lack of senior level health authority involvement in primary care groups suggests the primary care group is not key to the health authority's public health strategy.

While recognising that the majority of general practitioners in type A subscribe to a medical model of health, there is a danger of underestimating their interest in public health. Working with, or appearing to impose, a very different social model of health is likely to appear threatening and counterproductive. Initially it seems best to work with the medical model and to demonstrate the medical benefits to patients of an improved public health strategy.

Changing attitudes, culture and health ideologies need to be part of any strategy for developing greater public health involvement. There are no short cuts to this process – significant progress can be expected to take around two years for type A. Composition of the primary care group board is a key catalyst for change; lay members and other health professionals can provide the opportunity to filter in different perspectives and initiate partnerships; and where local networks develop they need effective health authority support to ensure they become a platform for future progress. Clinical governance with its associated peer pressure can be an important entry point to encourage more corporate thinking and strategic capacity.

B. Structure

Developing the structure is likely to be seen as a priority by health authorities. Getting the primary care group board right and supporting non-GP members to balance general practitioner dominance is most important. The concern here is the junior level of health authority representation with the primary care group board.

Structures in this type are weakened by political rivalries (especially between general practitioners over, for example, the position of Chair). These are best resolved by giving real responsibility which focuses attention on delivery. The health authority has an important initial role as power broker although there is a delicate balance between causing resentment by assuming the leadership role and creating a vacuum. There is a danger that the success of working with the board may result in board and member practices becoming misaligned.

C. Systems

The quality and nature of practice management varies widely in this type: fundholders, for example, may have well-developed systems, single-handers less so. System development is likely to be driven in response to external demands.

Practices are likely to prioritise practice investment (people and buildings) rather than primary care groups' overall systems development. Financing development out of savings allocated to a single development fund should encourage a more corporate approach. Given this potentially wide range of systems it is likely that initially only some practices would receive resources. Investment priorities need to be decided with reference to agreed minimum service standards.

D. Staff/skills

The focus is on the practice rather than primary care groups as a whole. Practices want to employ more of their own staff and to invest in skills (particularly clinical) and premises in order to develop primary care services as building blocks of primary care groups. They are willing to extend the practice team but probably not to include social services at this stage.

The ability to finance and recruit staff, however, is a problem, particularly in terms of recruiting nurses. Primary care groups here may look at strengthening the role of nurse practitioners and salaried doctors as a possible response to recruitment problems. Practices may also jointly commission services but are very reluctant to share staff in type A.

Type A primary care groups comprise those attracted by the security of retaining current roles and practices and limited organisational responsibility. They may actually recruit and retain staff who reinforce the model, making fundamental changes in culture more difficult. Threats to organisational viability such as capacity to recruit the right staff to deliver competitive services may be a key factor for change.

At a board level type A primary care groups have difficulty in getting sufficiently senior social services department representation, and sufficient early wins to retain them; and gain the full benefit of the influence for change their membership can bring.

E. Style

Mandated decision-making is sometimes idiosyncratic and autocratic. The primary care group board focus may be demotivating for non-general practitioner members who can become easily disillusioned. The seniority of representation is then likely to be downgraded.

There is, however, a positive potential in the general practitioner's therapeutic and individually oriented style, but more effort is needed to demonstrate that this style is appropriate and transferable to management issues.

F. Superordinate goal

This is quite simply the practice-based development of primary care.

Type B: The friendly society

A. Strategy

This primary care group is very 'inclusive' in its approach (that is including the views of all individual members – the whole primary care team). It wants to move forward from this organisational position, but is unclear how it will do this, or what it would wish to achieve. Some of the GPs have been working as a 'locality' group, 'co-commissioning' (in theory) with the health authority – although in reality, the latter have made the major commissioning decisions in the past. The health authority's views are accepted as an accurate reflection of local health needs although it is not clear whether they are 'evidence based', and the primary care group may want to challenge these as it becomes more established.

Type B, therefore, begins by thinking about access to services, rather than wider inequalities in health status. In terms of multi-agency work – there is no *local* strategic focus for this (that is at primary care level); joint health strategies have been very much at a high organisational level – between the health authority and the local authorities.

B. Structure

Type B focuses on its internal structure first, and its organisational development as a group (including skill mapping) to enable it to work towards becoming more public health focused. In the mean time it relies on its strong operational links at practice and inter-practice level to sustain local services.

C. Systems

The management challenge is considerable because of the broad-based approach, and ignorance about, for example, finance is high.

Accordingly, the priority is information including:

- understanding what information is collected (what do we want it for?)
- how is it collected?
- how is it used (including the interpretation and sharing of data)?
- what is known about the non-registered population.

The integration of information systems is a priority across the primary care group, with providers and with the health and local authorities, to ensure they are compatible with one another.

D. Style

The current style is 'inclusive' and the aim is to build on it, by extending the 'inclusiveness' to the partner organisations. This requires a 'developmental' perspective to move from 'where we are now, to where we want to be in three to five years' time'. The principles are:

- collaboration
- mutuality
- respect for others
- recognising and responding to diversity – of starting point and goals
- building on early successes.

A major concern is the tendency of policymakers/implementers to want to impose large organisational style, culture, and accountability frameworks on small organisations.

E. Skills

The need is for a number of basic management skills, including:

- change management
- organisational development
- influencing/challenging/changing clinical behaviour
- communications (all types, internal, external, up, down and sideways)
- information (gathering, analysis, dissemin-ation).

Strategically the priority is to develop skills around working in partnership with:

- local authorities
- NHS trusts
- the public.

And to move towards a population approach to commissioning with extra technical public health and advocacy skills.

The technical public health skills include:

- data collection (health status and health service use/effectiveness)
- data analysis and interpretation
- data use/dissemination (for commissioning purposes)
- health needs assessment.

The advocacy skills include developing the ability to influence:

- policies which impact on health, for example local authority housing, transport, environmental
- active public health (disease prevention) and health promotion, for example immunisation, vaccination, screening, healthy eating and smoking cessation.

Some of these will need to be available within the primary care group, and the type B board itself needs the following:

- ability to do 'joined-up' agendas
- ability to recognise the health impact of decisions on other parts of the system, and to deal with these jointly
- application of comparative data analysis.

The 'Friendly society' model relies on being self-contained in terms of doing its own planning, negotiating, financial control and organisational development.

F. Staff

Because of the reliance on the primary care group committee and practices themselves, this is hard to address. Type B talks about issues such as skill mix in primary care and continuing professional development, but uses advisory, and educational approaches rather than those of line or contract management. Often the hope of setting up new networks in the future means one person actually still has to do everything!

G. Superordinate goals

To change the commissioning process – to ensure it improves health as well as delivers services by shifting the budgets at health authority level and putting into effect what public health professionals have always advocated.

The priorities therefore are inherited from past local documents and focus on the national priorities of coronary heart disease (especially amongst ethnic minorities), mental health and teenage pregnancies. Early wins for the 'Friendly society' model are needed for:

- equity – within and across primary care groups
- needs-based prioritisation across primary care groups
- extending primary care services.

It is hoped that local links with, for example, individual cardiologists and headteachers can be used to build up goodwill and to engender a broad-based support for its general direction.

Type C: The executive agency

A. Strategy

Pragmatic, selective and focused are the epithets that capture this organisation's approach, which is based on 'doing deals' between clinicians with the positional power and personal influence to both change clinical practice and carry professional colleagues with them. Accordingly, the strategy of addressing 'head on' major rather than marginal targets for secondary to primary care transfers (for example A and E rather than maternity) is underpinned by a readiness to constrain GP referrals so that these resource shifts are not jeopardised. This is a health service rather than a health strategy.

B. Structure

The board consists of 'action men' (and it is overwhelmingly male). They personally put into effect the organisation's priorities. The board operates to a mandate from its constituents, regarding its successful fulfilment as the key to re-election. The GP quorum is all-powerful, and to promote secondary to primary care transfers, strong personal alliances are forged with lead social services managers/members in areas where local authorities have strong commissioning functions able to promote more community-based and integrated services. The wider GP constituency is content to let the board hit its targets without restrictions so long as resources continue to be diverted towards practices, and the political noise is manageable.

C. Systems

These are driven by a financial *motif*, looking particularly at cost savings in terms of single multi-PCG contracts, and procedures with hospitals and social services departments on such areas as cancer services, clinical governance and child protection. Savings are channelled into local practice-based primary care teams with carefully crafted joint funding arrangements with social services and community trust. A wide range of intermediate care facilities include dedicated GP beds in community hospitals, nursing and residential homes with local protocols for preventable A and E, acute episodes, in-patient continuing care and delayed discharges. Health targets of the Health Improvement Programmes only attract PCGs' marginal growth monies.

D. Staff

Leadership is by the few – mostly GPs and ex-GPFH leads – supported by strong data analysis and contracting staff posts. SSD representatives are fully co-opted into the PCG establishment and some consultants are placed on honorary contracts to ensure that they are on-side. Slim and lean in terms of numbers, maximising capacity of lead individual practice managers (with purchasing experience), and contracting for external resources wherever this represents value for money, this organisation is vigorous and flexible in its use of staff.

E. Skills

The strengths lie in information management and technology, data capture and analysis, commercial negotiating and political skills. The organisation is adept at managing interfaces, including upwards to the health authority and the NHS Executive, to ensure that sufficient space for independent action is protected. An effective time management approach is essential for board members whose own development programme ranges from the acquisition of short-term management skills to long-term leadership training.

F. Style

The board is motivated by a shared conviction of being 'the right people for the right job at the right time'. They are systematically opportunist and determined to exploit the health-care system in both professional and patient care interests. Their self-perception of board members is as 'go-getting social entrepreneurs' geared to delivery. They are ready to collaborate – to compete. The slogan is 'Ready to change to keep the best'.

G. Superordinate goals

To deliver effective health care

In terms of financial viability, interprofessional contributions and local access this is an important influence; but evidence-based medicine and special needs priorities are less significant factors.

To improve public health

This does not figure largely in terms of actual PCG behaviour. Improved health services are taken as the proxy, and public health attracts little direct resource investment.

Type D: The franchised public utility

A. Strategy

Its mission is to improve the health and wellbeing of the population and to reduce health inequalities and social exclusion. This language is important at this level because it incorporates the roles of both the Department of Health and local government, focusing on 'inequalities' as a joint and shared priority. It means the organisations need to engage in a bottom-up approach to assessing needs and selecting priorities and therefore to questioning 'old priorities'. The actual process of engaging communities is paramount, based on a range of methods which recognise the 'natural communities' that make up the population. Methods can include whole systems approaches, focus groups and citizens' juries.

Its specific strategies for priority areas span the full continuum of needs of population groups to improve their health and wellbeing, that is health services, local government services and community development. For example, plans for older people cover hip replacements, community safety, transport, housing, heating and social networks.

Its planning is based on the totality of NHS and local government resources and expenditure for the PCT population. It uses sophisticated programme planning techniques, for example health impact assessment analysis, to enable alternative investment strategies to be tested. All stakeholders, including communities, participate in debates about investment and rationing decisions. There is an increased awareness and ownership of resource consequences of investment choices. Balanced judgements that recognise the need to meet certain national standards and requirements as well as respond to local priorities characterise this level, as do different styles of service provision. The design and delivery of services based on new ways of involving individuals, families and communities include delegated budgets to communities; advocacy for isolated/vulnerable groups, and support to an infrastructure of community groups.

Concerned with ensuring that wider policies and strategies operate to promote the health and wellbeing of local communities and address inequalities, this organisation tests the boundaries of regulations and seeks freedoms to operate in more integrative and flexible ways. It recognises the need to ensure that quality standards and effective practice are adopted, for example via the National Institute for Clinical Excellence and that standards are universally available to socially excluded groups.

B. Structure

Type D tries to operate in a consensus way of working based on genuine partnership and a collaborative approach. It is concerned to increase democratic legitimisation and the accountability of the primary care organisation to the community through, for example, co-option of local government councillors to the board. It includes health, local government, community/voluntary sector, and local business representatives, and there is also a wide network of reference groups, supporting the board, representing and addressing the needs of specific groups and disparate communities.

C. Systems

It is essentially outward-looking. There are mechanisms for ensuring that the development and management of external relationships is strong. Initially however, less priority is given to the needs of the corporate infrastructure for supporting multi-practice/organisation functioning, and this causes internal stresses.

D. Staff/skills

The focus is on more generic 'primary care practitioners', based on a new range and mix of skills and expertise covering personal medical services, nursing, social care and community outreach and development; and on working in 'resource teams' serving different communities, and 'managed' by coordination. This represents a major shift from the traditional hierarchical structures and GP dominance. This is also a challenge to the 'independent practitioner' status, which is not obviously compatible with the new model for development and delivery of primary care services to communities. Accordingly the new organisational infrastructure is supported by a mix of specialist/management staff/skills: including project management, health planning, business management, public health specialisms and community development and outreach. It is flexible, ensuring that staff are responsive to changing needs and demands for different and diverse advice and expertise, with a balance between in-house and subcontracting/outsourcing.

E. Style

This can be termed 'corporatism with co-operation'. Formally the organisation is leading edge with 'beacon' status nationally. It seeks to be responsive, and open, emphasising convenience and flexibility, for example via a network of one-stop shops.

F. Culture

Overall the motivation is to 'make a difference' at community levels; with new indicators and mechanisms to define and provide feedback and learning on communities, as well as 'satisfaction' for individuals, whether professional, patients or members of the public.

Review

The organisational developments and their products described above are exciting. Overall, they suggest a new energy in the UK health system and a health system which is now beginning to embrace a much wider range of community interests. It is too soon, however, to be sure of either the specific outcomes or overall direction. Taking the strategic view for public health remains a major challenge for many in the NHS; and not just for those at the frontline of primary care.

The risks are formidable. At one end of the spectrum the 'Defence assoc iation' simply may not be capable of carrying individual general medical practitioners into the higher stages of primary care group development. Even at level 2 health authority managers may be unwilling or unable to delegate responsibilities, on grounds of both personal and performance preservation. The 'Executive agency' is an oligarchy with minimal commitment to the promotion of public health; and the type D primary care organisation is a massive management challenge, both internally and externally. How will it 'fit' with local authorities? What should be its framework for effective public accountabilities, not least in terms of its commissioning of its own primary care services?

Overall, however, the opportunities appear to outweigh the risks. Even those we met in this project dedicated to PCG development at level 1, had strengthened their focus on the individual patient and gained a greater appreciation of wider NHS issues and local priorities. Those aspiring to full primary care trust status, meanwhile, had clearly gained a considerable release. They were the minority, of course, but that is always true of strategists. They foresaw new primary care organisations as the means of empowering communities and radically reshaping services by linking the debate on 'rationing' restricted resources to new definitions and local priorities for public health.

For this hope to be realised, of course, there will need to be serious and substantial work at central policy levels. A number of significant policy issues have been highlighted in this project. The importance of new primary care organisations and public health initiatives aligning themselves together cannot be overstated. There is a danger of policy rhetoric outdistancing practical implementation. It is to this future agenda that we now turn our attention.

References

Boaden, N (1997). *Primary care*. Buckingham: Open University Press, p. 41.

Department of Health (1998). *The new NHS: modern. Dependable*. London: Stationery Office.

Dobson, Frank (1997). (Secretary of State for Health). Speech to NHS Confederation Annual Conference, Brighton.

Drucker, P (1995). *Post-capitalist society*. London: Fontana.

Edwards, A and Talbot, R (1994). *The hard-pressed researcher*. London: Longman, chapter 4.

Etzioni, A (1994). *The spirit of community*. London: Butterworth-Heinemann.

Iles, V (1997). *Really managing health care*. Buckingham: Open University Press, pp. 48–54.

Macdonald, J J (1992). *Primary health care*. London: Earthscan, pp. 85–139.

Mays, N and Dixon, J (1996). *Purchasing plurality in UK health care*. London: King's Fund.

NHS Executive (1996a). *Choice and opportunity*. London: Department of Health.

NHS Executive (1996b). *Primary care: the future*. London: Department of Health.

NHS Executive (1996c). *Delivering the future*. London: Department of Health.

NHS Executive (1998). *Establishing primary care groups*. Health Service Circular 1998/065. Leeds: NHSE.

Peters, T and Waterman, R (1980). 'Structure is not organisation'. In Quinn, J B and Mintzberg, H (eds) *The strategy process*. Englewood Cliffs, New Jersey: Prentice-Hall, pp. 309–14.

Starfield, B (1992). *Primary care: concept, evaluation and policy*. New York: Oxford University Press, pp. 3–87.

West Hertfordshire case study

Summary

A district of half a million population with five primary care groups. A traditional local authority structure of a county council and ten district councils (five within this health authority), with PCGs broadly coterminous with combinations of the latter. There was previously a single countywide health commission encompassing three district health authorities and one family health services authority.

Progress

Despite a number of organisational upheavals – which have attracted political and media attention nationally – there has been a significant long-term public health focus which has engaged a wide range of public service sectors including general practices. Fundamental to this progress have been the following:

- Feedback on morbidity/referral/social indices, etc. to general practices at local ward/parish level over several years (for example via the annual report of the director of public health).
- Readiness of Hertfordshire's social services to separate its own commissioning and providing functions and to organise around district council boundaries, in spite of reservations at county social services committee level.
- Presence of key individuals ready to campaign for deprived areas including certain lead GPs. Single Regeneration Budget (SRB) funding successfully obtained for Borehamwood, West Watford and South Oxhey, in part by using data from the director of public health.
- Inclusive district-wide approach of HA and previous health commission to whole GP community, both fundholders and non-fundholders, reflected in 16 GPs on West Hertfordshire's commissioning board that takes a genuine strategic stance on health priorities and service configuration (for example the conversion of St Albans Hospital from a district general hospital.
- The TPP example of St Albans which has maximised collaboration with the community health services and all practices on a discrete geographic basis, and has developed a genuine level 4 primary health care philosophy.
- The impetus provided by central policy pressures (for example the requirements for a HImP), which assists in areas as GP majority culture remains at heart that 'of only working together when a framework is imposed from above'.

Problems

Overwhelmingly the difficulties have arisen from recurrent organisational turbulence and the personal uncertainties arising from the turnover in agency structures. These have contributed to the following:

- An aggressive culture in terms of responding to central policies so that collaboration especially between practices (and the ever-changing health authority) is hard to achieve (for example one TPP dissolved as a result of the inter-practice differences).
- A strong loyalty and reliance on the individual practice unit, particularly amongst some fundholders.
- A continuing climate of competition and contracting, especially with hospital providers.
- Limited public health resources at the health authority.

'Central messages'

- The 'independent contractor' status consolidated by the national General Medical Services contract produces a basic business orientation, which is the greatest barrier to public health partnerships.
- The educational curriculum is the key to change.

(November 1998)

4. Reflections on the public health agenda

Primary care groups are a further stage in the decentralisation of the NHS. To a significant extent, because of their inherently mixed organisational status, they also represent a further stage in its deregulation. Together these developments represented for the participants in this project a major opportunity to extend effective support for strategies designed to enhance public health. But, of course, these opportunities come with their associated risks and resistance. Local resource management through primary care is bringing about the creation of new types of organisations, for which there are few reference points and no blueprints. The need to adopt a shared learning style supported by continuing evaluation and applied research was constantly emphasised.

> *'Primary care groups are a fundamental "mindset" change for individuals as well as organisations. The biggest obstacles are attitudinal not structural.'*
> (health authority director of public health)

In the past such statements have often led on to generalised exhortations for more interprofessional education, and joint audits or reviews; sometimes to little effect. The agenda is now more specific, driven by a sense of urgency in terms of understanding the practical benefits of the different relationships that will be required in the English health system. The following were identified as the key areas for examination where current practice is seen as lacking a coherent policy framework:

(i) the professional public health skills required of different types of primary care organisation, and their comparative utility in terms of health improvement

(ii) the interface between primary care organisations and local government, in terms of ensuring compatible and mutually reinforcing roles and responsibilities

(iii) the relative value of different partnerships for primary care groups with non-NHS organisations in relation to effective health strategy implementation

(iv) the relationships between primary care groups and other Family Health Services professionals (for example community pharmacists, dentists, optometrists); and the formal and informal mechanisms these will require to ensure the successful local co-ordination of health strategies

(v) the need to address the lack of organisational capacity of health authorities in terms of their future strategic performance management duties

and

(vi) the crucial future arrangements between health authorities and primary care organisations for effectively incorporating local development priorities, whilst ensuring that performance on centrally defined objectives is maintained.

'How long can health authorities be primary care group developers if they have to be NHS monitors as well?'

'How can we do organisational development for primary care when FHSA/DHA mergers have left us without an organisation'
(two health authority directors of primary care)

The last in the above list is all-important. It demonstrates the vital role of the Health Improvement Programme, as the source of overall direction for all the players in the local health system, whatever their status. This assertion has, of course, been frequently recognised and rehearsed. Where this project goes further is in suggesting that there are two prerequisites essential to the success of HImPs. These are:

(i) the need to support health strategies with a *real commitment to the different working relationships* they require; and
(ii) the need for a *nationwide framework of local mechanisms* for promoting and delivering primary health care based on the principles of inter-agency working, community involvement and equity, and ranging from specific service contracts to new partnership covenants.

The second is the most pressing priority. An inventory of current good practice in terms of PCG-level operational agreements for health improvement could be a useful starting point; and offer a valuable opportunity for many NHS community trusts to become positively engaged on the public health agenda.

At present the national terms of service for general medical practitioners and other Family Health Services professionals are administrative in character, with little explicit health promotion content. They are often best regarded as the lowest common denominator. The post-April 1997 Primary Care Act pilot sites would, of course, be included in such an inventory. However, these are essentially, for the most part, one-off service developments rather than public health initiatives. There are exceptions, including most obviously those schemes dedicated to primary health care for homeless people, but the majority of PCAPs are either focused on the individual practice or practitioner (for example the salaried GP or nurse practitioner.) They do not, therefore, give a true representation of local developments in terms of local primary health-care contracts such as that referred to above in respect of Nottingham's general practices and schools for local health education; or the comprehensive local community pharmacy health-care accreditation scheme operated by Dorset Health Authority. New primary care organisations will only be able to contribute to improved public health as well as deliver effective health care if the commissioning functions develop in such a way that a full range of primary health-care contractual processes and mechanisms becomes available.

'We need to re-engage trusts (including acute hospitals) as partners, and educate them on the health agenda'
(HA director of commissioning)

The same new level of attention also now needs to be paid to the management of relationships. Health and relationships are indivisible. Despite a real thirst for understanding in this area, however, the extent to which participants in the project's twelve districts either knew of robust approaches to inter-agency collaboration and interprofessional partnerships, or then applied them in practice, was strictly limited. Fortunately the relevant applied academic literature in this field is expanding. The box opposite, for example, provides a valuable insight into working with the independent sector based on Maureen Devlin's recent studies of primary care partnerships with the private sector (Devlin, 1998). Bob Hudson (1998) at Leeds and Hugh Barr (1995) at Westminster similarly have developed empirically sound criteria for collaboration and interactive learning respectively between primary and social care staff. Increasingly there is little excuse for regarding the new partnerships' language of public health as political rhetoric. The sources of the different kinds of leadership and behaviours it requires are available. The message from this project was not just 'Go, look, see' but 'Act!' The new responsibilities of primary care groups for public health are a genuine opportunity to move from dialogue to deeds.

Partnerships

Work because:

- Individual and joint objectives coincide
- Reciprocity becomes the driving force
- Process is managed with internal review milestones and external success markers
- Common 'enemy' remains to the fore
- Damage limitation strategy is held in reserve.

Source: Devlin (1998)

The final message from the project for those engaged in policy formulation is, inevitably, about resources. As health authorities learn their new roles, there is in many areas a risk of local hiatus. One chief executive referred to the new health authority role as that of 'indirect' leadership, like that of a second violin in a string quintet. But promoting public health through primary care organisations may require the full orchestra in all its parts. It must not simply be left to a few virtuoso performances.

In every part of the country there will need to be skilled, experienced conductors to get the pace, balance and timing just right. This will not simply happen through exhortation. A lot of rehearsals, many failures and considerable investments of time, money and professional resources are required. If these needs are not addressed the question will not be 'How?' but still 'Can new primary care organisations improve public health as well as deliver effective health care?'

References

Barr, H (1995). *Perspectives in shared learning.* London: CAIPE.

Devlin, M (1998). *Primary health care and the private sector.* Oxford: Radcliffe Medical Press, pp. 65–8.

Hudson, R (1998). *Primary care and social care.* Leeds: Nuffield Institute.

Appendices

Appendix A Health strategy framework

How can primary care organisations improve the health of local communities?

A framework to enable project participants to reach an initial position statement on working together to develop local health strategy and health improvement plans

Background

This framework has been produced as part of a development project, funded by the Health Education Authority, to examine how the new primary care groups (primary care organisations) can contribute to the development of a strategic approach to improving the health of their local communities, through informing health authority Health Improvement Programmes and implementing local health action plans.

The purpose of this framework is to

- enable the project team to gather some baseline information on the current state of health strategy development at a local level
- enable project participants to set the agenda for discussion with partner organisations around the skills, resources and support they already have available, or will need to develop, to enable them to contribute effectively to the development and implementation of local Health Improvement Programmes and action plans.

Notes on using the framework

There are a range of possible answers to all the questions used in the framework. Please answer these in the way that you feel is most appropriate to your organisation and local circumstances. Notes and follow-on questions are included for guidance; they are not intended to be prescriptive. If you feel there is something important which we have not included, please do let us know, so that we can pick this up at the next stage of the project.

It would be helpful if you could include a summary response to each question in the space provided. However, the project team would also be happy to receive fuller responses where you feel this would be appropriate. You may also wish to include supporting documentation where this is available and relevant to your response.

Question	Follow-up questions and notes	Response
1. How do you think your local health strategy and priorities will change or develop in response to (a) *Our healthier nation*? (b) developing your local Health Improvement Programme?	If you have not yet seen/had time to consider the implications of the White Paper, please describe any initial thoughts about what you would like to happen, based on your experience to date (including previous health strategies, such as Health of the Nation, and initial work on developing your Health Improvement Programme).	
2. What are your key priorities/target areas for (a) improving health? (b) reducing inequalities in health status	Please list these. Would you describe these as predominantly – disease-based? (e.g. CHD, asthma) – client group-based? (the elderly, children) – addressing the wider determinants of health? (such as inequalities, poor housing, air quality)	
3. What will these priorities be based on?	What will the balance be between national (*Our healthier nation*) targets and local targets? Will these be derived from — local demography — population-based needs assessment — practice-based needs assessment — priorities for partner organisation (e.g. local authority, NHS trust, primary care) — local political priorities — evidence of effective interventions — national/local research — other? (please describe)	
4. How will these be agreed?	i.e. who will be involved in deciding what to prioritise and how will this process take place? Include information about any — initial discussions — wider consultation process — unsolicited responses.	
5. What approach will you take to working with your local primary care organisation or health authority on *Our healthier nation*?	Remember to think about approaches to — the consultation process — the development of a Health Improvement Programme — implementation of local health action plans. (It is appreciated that at this point, some of this will be at a very early stage of development.)	
6. What support do you think primary care groups will need to contribute effectively to the development and implementation of HImPs and action plans?	This may include support to develop or use — public health skills and knowledge — information sources — research evidence as well as — organisational development — education and training — personal and professional development.	

Question	Follow-up questions and notes	Response
7. What resources are currently available to support this work? Where are these resources located?	'Resources' here is taken to include — knowledge/skills — people — budgets — information sources — other (e.g. existing alliances). Remember to think about what is available — within and across the health authority (not only in the public health department) — within trusts (especially where Health Promotion is located in a trust) — within primary care organisations (remember the whole primary care team) — within other organisations (e.g. local academic department, local authority, voluntary/non-statutory organisations) — within the wider community.	
8. What specific mechanisms/ processes do you currently have in place for joint working to improve the health of your local communities?	Include informal as well as formal processes, as appropriate, for working jointly with — health authority — primary care organisations — trusts — local authorities — non-statutory/voluntary sector — wider community.	
9. How do you think the new primary care organisations will be able to influence the setting of local priorities/target areas?	i.e. in addition to those selected as national priorities/targets within *Our healthier nation*?	

Appendix B Relational profiling: a questionnaire for health authorities and primary care organisations

CONFIDENTIAL

How can primary care organisations improve public health as well as deliver health care?

Thank you for agreeing to complete this questionnaire. It asks about your experience of relating to the key people you deal with in the health authority/PCO in relation to the above question. It is intended to provide a simple stock-take of the relationship. This will be the basis for looking at how the relationship could be developed to enable primary care organisations to be more involved in improving public health as well as delivering health care.

Please tick only one box for each question. There are no right or wrong answers. It is your own honest opinion that matters.

	Strongly agree	Slightly agree	Neither agree nor disagree	Slightly disagree	Strongly disagree
1. I can get in touch when I need to	☐	☐	☐	☐	☐
2. We are in contact often enough to maintain a good working relationship	☐	☐	☐	☐	☐
3. Not enough attention is paid to long-term issues	☐	☐	☐	☐	☐
4. The constraints on what I can contribute to public health are understood	☐	☐	☐	☐	☐
5. We have a good knowledge of each other as individuals	☐	☐	☐	☐	☐
6. We both benefit from greater involvement by primary care organisations in public health	☐	☐	☐	☐	☐
7. I am treated courteously and with respect	☐	☐	☐	☐	☐
8. We combine our different skills and perspectives to make a positive contribution to public health	☐	☐	☐	☐	☐
9. Our goals for the development of this relationship are different	☐	☐	☐	☐	☐
10. My messages and questions are responded to promptly	☐	☐	☐	☐	☐
11. Information is best gained through informal channels	☐	☐	☐	☐	☐

Please turn over

	Strongly agree	Slightly agree	Neither agree nor disagree	Slightly disagree	Strongly disagree
12. We can be open with one another	☐	☐	☐	☐	☐
13. New staff are quick to pick up on the key issues	☐	☐	☐	☐	☐
14. I have a say in decisions which affect my work	☐	☐	☐	☐	☐
15. Responsibility is fairly shared	☐	☐	☐	☐	☐
16. The interests of our own organisations can impede partnership	☐	☐	☐	☐	☐
17. Our priorities for public health are very different	☐	☐	☐	☐	☐
18. There are enough opportunities for us to meet face to face	☐	☐	☐	☐	☐
19. I often hear about decisions which affect my work via the grapevine	☐	☐	☐	☐	☐
20. Any concerns I may have are picked up on quickly	☐	☐	☐	☐	☐
21. We have been working together long enough to develop a good understanding	☐	☐	☐	☐	☐
22. Poor internal communication hampers our relationship	☐	☐	☐	☐	☐
23. We have an all-round picture of each other's particular work interests	☐	☐	☐	☐	☐
24. We respect each other's different views and contributions	☐	☐	☐	☐	☐
25. This is a long-term relationship	☐	☐	☐	☐	☐
26. Our understanding of health is basically the same	☐	☐	☐	☐	☐

27. Which organisation do you work for?

28. What is your job title?

Please return your completed questionnaire to Professor Geoff Meads, Health Management Group, City University, Northampton Square, London EC1V 0HB.

Appendix C Relational profile: worked example from a participating health district

Relational profile of a health authority and primary care group: one example

The relational profile is designed to highlight those aspects of the relationship which may be regarded as a cause for concern. The questionnaire was completed by one representative from each organisation. The results will therefore not necessarily reflect other people's experience of the relationship but do provide a baseline for further discussion and reflection.

Overview of relationship

The health authority's (HA's) perception of the relationship is more positive than average, particularly with regard to the degree of directness and commonality in the relationship. It is also in these two aspects of the relationship that the HA view diverges from that of the primary care organisation (PCO).

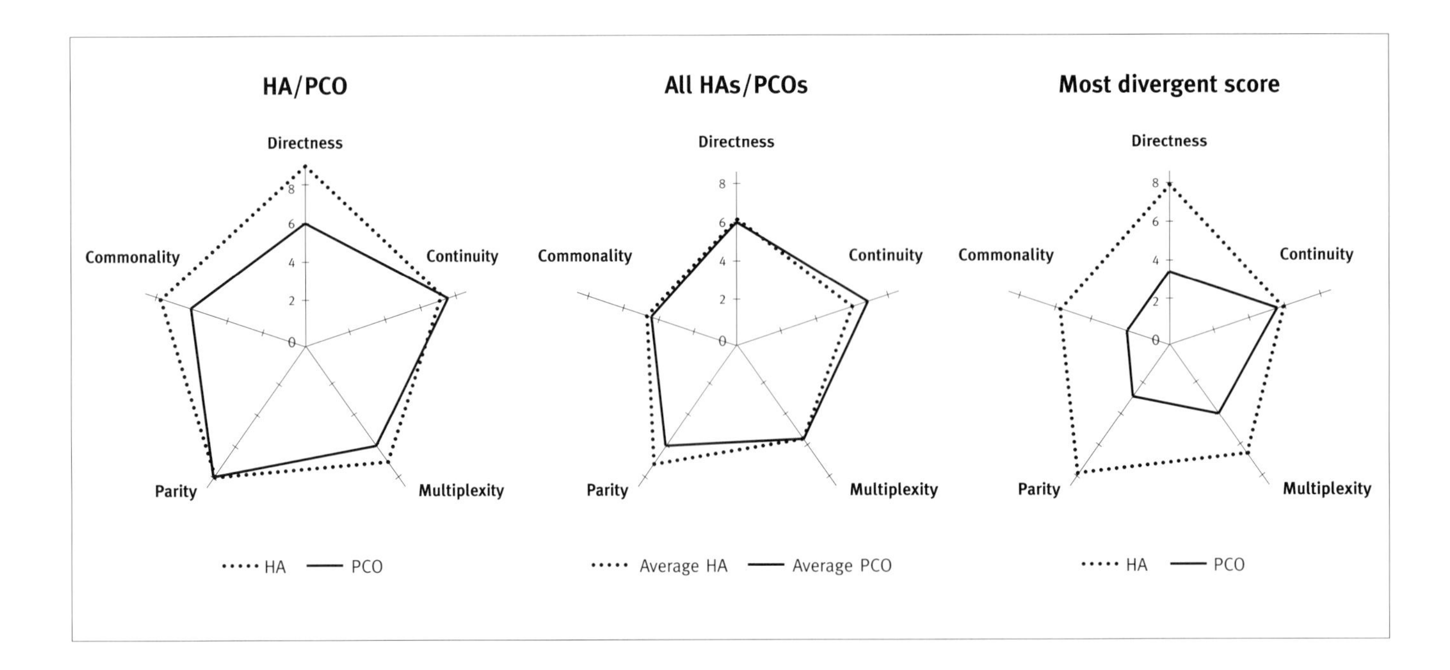

Directness

Directness is concerned with the quality of the communication process. The HA was strongly positive on all aspects of this relationship. The PCO view was generally only slightly positive. The one issue on which there were differing views was on whether decisions were heard via the grapevine.

	Strongly agree	Slightly agree	Neither agree or disagree	Slightly disagree	Strongly disagree
I can get in touch when I need to	● Local HA, ■ Local PCO, Average PCO	Average HA			
My messages and questions are responded to promptly	● Local HA	■ Local PCO, Average PCO, Average HA			
I often hear about decisions which affect my work via the grapevine		■ Local PCO	Average PCO	Average HA	● Local HA
We can be open with one another	● Local HA	Average HA	Average PCO, ■ Local PCO		
Any concerns I may have are picked up on quickly	● Local HA	■ Local PCO, Average HA	Average PCO		
There are enough opportunities for us to meet face to face	● Local HA	■ Local PCO, Average HA/Average PCO coincide			

● Local HA ■ Local PCO Average HA Average PCO Average HA/Average PCO coincide

Continuity

Time is the currency of relationships. The amount of contact and the length of the relationships are important for building trust and understanding. There is some concern that not enough attention is paid to long-term issues.

	Strongly agree	Slightly agree	Neither agree or disagree	Slightly disagree	Strongly disagree
We are in contact often enough to maintain a good working relationship	■ Local PCO, ● Local HA, Average HA	Average PCO			
Not enough attention is paid to long-term issues		● Local HA, Average PCO, Average HA	■ Local PCO		
We have been working together long enough to develop a good understanding	■ Local PCO	● Local HA, Average HA	Average PCO		
This is a long-term relationship	■ Local PCO, ● Local HA, Average HA	Average PCO			
New staff are quick to pick up on the key issues		● Local HA	Average PCO, ■ Local PCO, Average HA		

● Local HA ■ Local PCO Average HA Average PCO

Multiplexity

Breadth of knowledge – of the other party, their role and their constraints – aids the management of the relationships and aids team effectiveness. Both HA and PCO views are slightly above average. A possible concern for the PCO is whether the constraints on what they can contribute to public health are understood.

	Strongly agree	Slightly agree	Neither agree or disagree	Slightly disagree	Strongly disagree
The constraints on what I can contribute to public health are understood		●	■ ▒		
We have a good knowledge of each other as individuals		● ■ ▒			
We have an all-round picture of each other's particular work interests		● ■	▒		

● Local HA ■ Local PCO Average HA ▒ Average PCO

Parity

Parity is concerned with participation and fairness in the relationship. HA and PCO views were similar with no concerns being expressed.

	Strongly agree	Slightly agree	Neither agree or disagree	Slightly disagree	Strongly disagree
We both benefit from greater involvement by primary care organisations in public health		● ■ ▒			
I am treated courteously and with respect	● ■ ▒				
We respect each other's different views and contribution		● ■ ▒			
I have a say in decisions which affect my work	■	●	▒		
Responsibility is fairly shared	●	■	▒		

● Local HA ■ Local PCO Average HA ▒ Average PCO

Commonality

Real common purpose is an important foundation for working together. Together with directness this was the aspect of the relationship where there was greatest divergence of view. The HA's only concern was that organisational interests could impede partnership. The PCO was less strongly positive and uncertain as to whether goals for the development of the relationship and priorities for public health were shared.

	Strongly agree	Slightly agree	Neither agree or disagree	Slightly disagree	Strongly disagree
Our understanding of health is basically the same	● Local HA	■ Local PCO, Average HA, Average PCO			
We combine our different skills and perspectives to make a positive contribution to public health	● Local HA	■ Local PCO, Average HA	Average PCO		
Our goals for the development of this are different		Average HA	■ Local PCO, Average PCO		● Local HA
The interests of our own organisations impede partnership		Average HA, Average PCO, ● Local HA	■ Local PCO		
Our priorities for public health are very different		Average PCO	■ Local PCO, Average HA		● Local HA

● Local HA ■ Local PCO Average HA Average PCO

General

Where informal communication channels are important (as in this case) it is important that these benefits are not lost when staff change, and that formal channels are not undermined. Weaknesses in internal communication were not felt to pose a problem for this relationship.

	Strongly agree	Slightly agree	Neither agree or disagree	Slightly disagree	Strongly disagree
Information is best gained through informal channels		■ Local PCO, ● Local HA, Average HA	Average PCO		
Poor internal communication hampers our relationship			Average PCO, Average HA	■ Local PCO	● Local HA

● Local HA ■ Local PCO Average HA Average PCO